INTERNATIONAL SERIES OF MONOGRAPHS IN

ANALYTICAL CHEMISTRY

GENERAL EDITORS: R. BELCHER AND H. FREISER

VOLUME 17

Gas Analysis by
Gas Chromatography

OTHER TITLES IN THE SERIES IN
ANALYTICAL CHEMISTRY

Gas Analysis by Gas Chromatography

SECOND EDITION

BY

P. G. JEFFERY

Senior Principal Scientific Officer, Warren Spring Laboratory,
Department of Trade and Industry

AND

P. J. KIPPING

Senior Experimental Officer, Warren Spring Laboratory,
Department of Trade and Industry

PERGAMON PRESS

OXFORD · NEW YORK · TORONTO
SYDNEY · BRAUNSCHWEIG

Pergamon Press Ltd., Headington Hill Hall, Oxford

Pergamon Press Inc., Maxwell House, Fairview Park, Elmsford,
New York 10523

Pergamon of Canada Ltd., 207 Queen's Quay West, Toronto 1

Pergamon Press (Aust.) Pty. Ltd., 19a Boundary Street,
Rushcutters Bay, N.S.W. 2011, Australia

Vieweg & Sohn GmbH, Burgplatz 1, Braunschweig

First edition 1964

Second edition 1972

Library of Congress Catalog Card No. 72–180544

Printed in Great Britain by A. Wheaton & Co., Exeter

08 016808 6

Contents

Preface

GASEOUS mixtures are of considerable importance in industry, where they are used in vast quantities as fuels and as raw materials and are produced in even greater quantities as the waste products of combustion and of manufacturing processes of many kinds.

The traditional chemical methods of analysis, with which the names of Bunte, Hempel, Orsat, Bone and Wheeler, and Haldane are associated, have for many years been used to examine towns' gas, water gas, flue gases, vehicle engine exhaust gases, furnace gases and many other such mixtures. With the increasing complexity of modern industrial processes and the increasing use of less common gases, the traditional chemical methods, which were rarely specific, are no longer adequate. In the last few years many of these older chemical methods have been replaced by rapid, more specific and often very much more convenient methods based upon gas chromatography.

For example, in the field of hydrocarbon gas analysis, it is now possible to determine quantitatively all the compounds in the range C_1 to C_4, using less than a millilitre of sample in a matter of a few minutes. Previously this analysis required extensive fractionation, used large sample aliquots and took many hours for a single determination. The results of these older laborious separations were always very inferior to those that can now be obtained by using gas chromatography.

The speed with which chromatographic separations can be obtained, and the ease with which detector signals can be registered and repeated, has led to the adoption of this technique as a means of process control. Not all chromatographic separations can be operated automatically, and the best examples of processes that are already controlled in this way are those in which hydrocarbon gases are involved, for example in the large scale production of ethylene.

We are grateful to the Director, Warren Spring Laboratory for permission to reproduce published and unpublished work of the Laboratory and to the various authors and editors for permission to reproduce copyright material; the source of each contribution is acknowledged in the text. In particular we would like to thank those who wrote personally to us with helpful comments and suggestions. We are also grateful to Janet Kipping who undertook the tedious task of compiling the index.

This book is written for the analyst as a guide to the determination of the various components of the common gaseous mixtures, and is concerned primarily with the practical aspects of this particular application of gas chromatography. A theoretical treatment of separation by gas–liquid or gas–solid chromatography is rarely of direct help to the practising analyst—at least at the present time—and for that reason has not been included here. Another aspect of this rapidly developing subject that has not been included in this present volume is the design of the electronic circuitry for use with ionization detectors. At one time familiarity with a simple Wheatstone bridge was the only experience required to undertake the wiring of a chromatograph. The design and construction of the amplifier, high voltage direct current supply, temperature programme units and other electrical devices that are incorporated into a modern gas chromatograph are, however, best left to the electronic engineer and instrument manufacturer.

It is felt, however, that every analyst using this technique should at least know how to use the detectors that are now available, and be able to select the best for a particular application. Similarly from the same viewpoint, the precise mechanism by which chromatographic separation takes place on the surface of the active material is not important, provided that the appropriate column packing can be selected.

In common with many others, we have had some difficulty in defining a "gas", and deciding at what point in a homologous series the compounds are best considered as volatile liquids. To some extent this is of academic interest only, as many of the volatile liquids are easily handled in the gaseous state. We have included in this book reference to those compounds that are normally transferred to a gas chromatograph in the gaseous state and are present in such samples in amounts that warrant determination.

This loose interpretation has enabled us to include the determination of water vapour, present to some extent in almost all gas samples, as well as the hydrocarbons in the C_5 range that occur in fuel gas mixtures. Even so, the choice of compounds with boiling points above normal room temperature must inevitably be coloured by our own experience.

All temperatures are quoted in degrees centigrade (Celsius), and where other scales have been used in the original papers, we have converted the figures quoted to the centigrade scale. It is customary in reporting gas analyses to express the concentrations in terms of volumes, either volume per cent, or parts per million by volume. This use has been followed throughout.

The first part of this book is devoted to a description of the apparatus used for gas chromatography. In the following part the methods used for the determination of the individual gases are described, including wherever possible details of the operating conditions necessary. It must be remembered, however, that many of these separations depend upon the use of activated solid adsorbents, and that it is difficult to reproduce the active state of such materials. Finally, in the concluding part, some examples are given of the analysis of specific mixtures, and of the recovery of gaseous constituents from solid and liquid materials, together with a few notes on the sampling of gaseous mixtures.

PART I

CHAPTER 1

Introduction

History

Chromatography is a process of separation, achieved by means of a partition between a stationary phase and a moving phase. The possibility of using a gas as the moving phase was forecast by Martin and Synge [1] in 1941 at the time of introducing liquid–liquid chromatography. It was not until 1952, however, that Martin, this time with James [2], published the results of the first successful experiments in gas–liquid chromatography. From this conception and introduction, the use of gas chromatography rapidly spread, to be used for separations that were hitherto regarded as tedious, difficult or even impossible, and achieving these with simplicity and elegance. No other analytical technique had spread so rapidly or become popular in so short a time, giving rise to an extensive literature ranging from patents and original papers to books, journals and reviews. In this time great improvements have been made in the design of sampling systems, efficiencies of chromatographic columns and in the selection of stationary phases. However, the greatest improvement has been in the design and development of new detectors with increased sensitivity and selectivity. Some of these detectors, particularly the argon ionization detector and the flame ionization detector, are extremely sensitive to volatile organic compounds, for which chromatographic separation can often be employed. This combination of high sensitivity with ready separation completely revolutionized the methods used for the analysis of liquid organic materials, as, for example, in the petroleum industry, where a very high proportion of the older methods are now obsolete.

The introduction of new types of gaseous fuel and of less well-known gaseous raw materials in industry and commerce rendered obsolete many of the traditional methods used for gas analysis. The advantages of speed, specificity and simplicity offered have resulted in increasing interest in gas chromatography for this purpose. This use, although not as widely known as the analysis of volatile organic liquids, is one of the rapidly developing applications of gas chromatography at the present time. In this new edition, the opportunity has been taken of adding new material to most of the chapters, of bringing the bibliographies and examples up to date and of revising the original text where this has become necessary.

3

Definitions

The need to standardize the use of terms has been evident from the time that gas chromatography ceased to be the province of a few enthusiastic experimenters, and became accepted as yet another important analytical tool.

A number of organizations have considered the terminology used for gas chromatography. Amongst these are the Gas Chromatography Discussion Group under the auspices of the Hydrocarbon Research Group of the Institute of Petroleum, the Research Division IV of the ASTM Committee of Petroleum Products and Lubricants, the International Union of Pure and Applied Chemistry and the British Standards Institution.

Since the first edition of this book was prepared, the British Standards Institution has issued a revised Glossary of Terms Relating to Gas Chromatography, BS 3282:1969, from which the following definitions have been taken.

Gas chromatography: Any method of chromatography in which the mobile phase is a gas.

Gas–liquid chromatography: Any method of gas chromatography in which the stationary phase is a liquid distributed on a solid support.

Gas–solid chromatography: Any method of gas chromatography in which the stationary phase is an active solid.

Liquid phase: A substance which is liquid but substantially non-volatile at the column temperature and is sorbed on the solid support.

Active solid: A solid with sorptive properties which differ for various components of the sample.

Modified sorbent: An active solid whose activity has been limited by the addition of a modifying liquid.

Stationary phase: The liquid phase, the active solid or the modified sorbent.

Solid support: Normally an inert solid which supports the stationary phase. In some gas–liquid methods the solid support may also be an active solid. The wall of the column contributes to the solid support.

Packing: The stationary phase, including any solid support, with which a chromatographic column may be filled.

Mobile phase: The gas passing through a chromatographic column.

Carrier gas: The gas used to transport the sample through the column.

Auxiliary gas: A gas other than the carrier gas which is necessary for the functioning of the detector.

Internal standard: A compound added to a sample in known concentration for the purpose of eliminating the need to measure the size of sample injected for quantitative analysis.

Marker: A compound of known retention time, added to a sample to assist in identifying the components.

Backflush: The reversal of direction of flow through the column, after some components have been eluted, to remove those of long retention time.

Sample injector: A device by which a sample is introduced into the carrier gas stream.

Bypass injector: A sample injector by means of which the carrier gas can be temporarily diverted through a sample chamber, thus causing the sample to be carried to the column.

Column: The portion of the apparatus in which chromatographic separation occurs.

Adsorption column: A column containing an active solid.

Partition column: A column containing an inert solid support coated with a liquid phase.

Packed column: A column filled with packing.

Open tubular column: A column containing stationary phase but having an unobstructed axial channel.

Capillary column: A column of capillary dimensions, generally less than 1 mm internal diameter.

Detector: A device whose response is dependent on the composition of the column effluent.

Differential detector: A detector whose response is dependent on the instantaneous difference in composition between the column effluent and the carrier gas.

Integral detector: A detector whose response is dependent on the total amount of a component passing through it.

Chromatogram: A graphical or other presentation of detector signal against time or against volume of carrier gas. (Methods of presentation other than graphical are preferably described as chromatographic records.)

Base line: The portion of the chromatogram produced under operating conditions when no component is emerging from the column.

Peak: The portion of a differential chromatogram showing the response when a component of the sample emerges from the column (*CED*, Fig. 1).

Peak base: An interpolation, between the extremities of the peak, of the line which a differential chromatogram would have followed if the sample component under which the peak base is drawn had not been present (*CD*, Fig. 1).

Peak area: The area enclosed between the peak and the peak base (*CHEJDC*, Fig. 1).

Peak height: The intercept on the ordinate between the peak maximum and the peak base (*BE*, Fig. 1).

Peak width: The projection of the horizontal axis of the segment of the peak base intercepted between tangents to the inflection points of the peak (*FG*, Fig. 1).

Peak width at half height: The horizontal distance (*PQ*, Fig. 1) between two vertical lines of half peak height (*PH*, *QJ*) joining the peak to the peak base.

Step: The change of base line position in an integral chromatogram caused by the elution of a component of the sample (*L* to *M*, Fig. 1).

Step height: The difference in value of the ordinate before and after a step (*KL* or *LM*, Fig. 1).

Retention time (t_R): The time between injection of the sample and emergence of the peak maximum of a stated component (*OB*, Fig. 1; on a time scale).

Retention volume (V_R): The volume of carrier gas passing through the column between the injection of the sample and the emergence of the peak maximum of a stated component (*OB*, Fig. 1; on a volume scale; $V_R = t_R F_c$, where F_c = carrier gas flow rate).

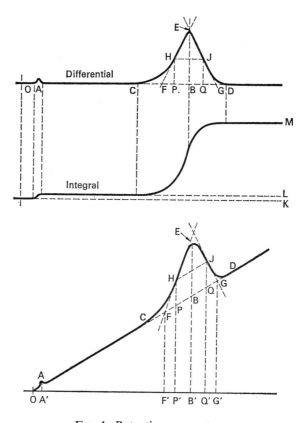

FIG. 1. Retention parameters.

Principles

Chromatography is essentially a separating procedure, but it can also be used to isolate or confirm components present in complex mixtures. The ease with which two closely related compounds can be resolved has led to the use of gas chromatography for the purification of organic materials on a preparative scale, and many compounds available at the present time are described as "chromatographically pure", i.e. they give only a single peak when analysed in this way. However the outstanding contribution of gas chromatography is in the field of qualitative and more particularly quantitative analysis.

The mixture under investigation is injected, either directly or by using a by-pass chamber, into a stream of carrier gas at the head of a column of separating medium. This medium can be either a solid adsorbent such as charcoal, or a liquid dispersed on an inert solid such as glycerol on firebrick. The sample mixture is swept by the carrier gas on to the column, where the various components are separated from each other. Some components may be swept through the column without being retarded, some may be completely absorbed by it, whilst others will undergo partition between the separation medium and the carrier gas, and be separated from other compounds present during the progress along the chromatographic column. Occasionally two components will be retarded to the same extent and will then be eluted from the column together. This process of chromatographic separation is a complex one, and although the theory is now well developed, all or almost all of the separations used in practice were first developed and exploited empirically.

In the carrier gas stream leaving the column are firstly any sample components not retarded, and then in turn the components fractionated during passage through the column. The presence of these sample components in the stream of carrier gas is indicated by the detector, from which a response is obtained corresponding to changes of a suitable property of the carrier gas, for example of thermal conductivity. This response is usually converted to an electrical signal for ease of recording.

The essential parts of any chromatograph are therefore a carrier gas stream, a sample inlet mechanism, a chromatographic column, and a detector. In order to obtain reproducible results a thermostat is also necessary, whilst a strip chart potentiometric recorder is also usually regarded as an essential item.

CHAPTER 2

Sample Transfer Systems

THE purpose of a sample system is to transfer a measured amount of the sample material, usually between 0·1 and 10 ml, into the stream of carrier gas in a quantitative and reproducible way, avoiding contamination and interfering as little as possible with the flow of carrier gas.

One of the conditions for maximum chromatographic response is that the sample shall be contained in the smallest possible column volume. For this reason the sampling system must ensure the transfer of the measured sample aliquot into the stream of carrier gas as rapidly as possible. Speed is also essential when flame methods are used, as the flow of hydrogen or hydrogen–nitrogen mixture used as carrier gas must not be interrupted for more than a very brief period. This danger of extinguishing the flame can be avoided by using nitrogen as carrier gas in conjunction with a separate hydrogen gas supply which is mixed with the carrier gas and sample components at the exit from the column, in a position immediately before the detector.

A number of sample transfer devices has been described; some of these are of general application, whilst others are suited only for particular examples, such as from piped sample supplies. These devices can conveniently be considered in the following groups:

Direct injection into the carrier gas stream.
The use of by-pass sample loops with constant volume pipettes or with syringe injection.
Automatic and semi-automatic devices.
Miscellaneous methods.

Direct Injection into the Carrier Gas Stream

This is the simplest form of sample transfer. The aliquot for analysis is taken from the sample container or from the piped supply into a gas-tight syringe. The hypodermic needle of the syringe is then inserted into the stream of carrier gas through a serum cap or a silicone rubber septum. The contents of the syringe are then discharged into the carrier gas.

This method of sample introduction is used extensively where only qualitative or approximate results are required. Experiments with syringes to which hypodermic needles had been fitted have shown that such an injection cannot be accomplished in a quantitative or reproducible way if the carrier gas pressure is

8

much above atmospheric. This method of sample addition cannot therefore be recommended where any degree of accuracy is wanted or where the determinations required include constituents present in major proportions.

Use of By-pass Sample Loops

Constant Volume Pipettes

A typical constant volume pipette in a by-pass sample loop is shown in Fig. 2 [3]. To use this device it is necessary to determine the volume of the pipette, to displace all the air initially present with a sufficiently large volume of the sample, and

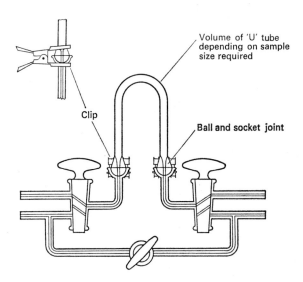

FIG. 2. A constant volume sample pipette (Institute of Petroleum, Standards for Petroleum and its products).

finally to determine the pressure of the gas sample in the pipette before transferring it to the carrier gas stream. The useful volume range of this device can be varied from less than 0·1 ml to about 10 ml by appropriate choice of U-tube. These may be fabricated from short lengths of capillary glass tubing, long lengths of wide-bore tubing or from bulb sections as shown in Fig. 3.

By-pass pipettes of this kind are available in glass or metal. Experience with a commercially available metal sampling valve has shown that it is difficult to ensure that it is leak-proof. In spite of difficulties of this kind, both glass and metal pipettes are popular in that they are robust, easy to calibrate and do ensure that reproducible amounts of sample material can be taken.

Disadvantages of this type of sampling device are that a volume calibration is required, carefully prepared gas mixtures are necessary for detector calibration, the volume of sample gas required to purge the pipette is large in relation to the volume required for analysis, and it is necessary to turn a minimum of three taps to admit the gas sample to the chromatograph. Such valves find their greatest use where the analysis required is that of a piped supply.

Although it is more usual to vary the size of sample taken by choosing an appropriate size of loop, the amount of sample can be increased by operating the sampling line at a higher pressure. The limiting pressure is, however, soon reached

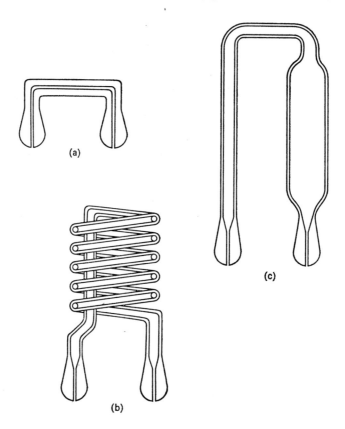

FIG. 3. "U-tubes" for use with by-pass sample loops (after Forss, Bazinet and Swift, *J. Gas Chromatog*. 1964).

with glass taps, even when they are spring loaded. For calibration purposes the sample loop shown in Fig. 4 can be used in conjunction with the by-pass shown in Fig. 2, to deliver into the carrier gas stream any of a small number of fixed volumes. Such devices are preferably used in conjunction with a piped supply, but the sample aliquot can be taken from a container with the static supply at atmospheric pressure. The whole of the by-pass sample loop is first evacuated, then filled with the sample material. The gas pressure in the loop is determined, the required sample aliquot isolated, and the remainder of the sample in the loop removed by evacuating both ends of the loop line.

This device is difficult to make, easy to break, awkward to mount and cumbersome to use. An accurate volume calibration is required, and the glass taps require

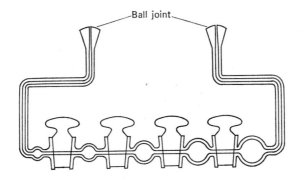

FIG. 4. A calibration pipette. This pipette, used in place of the sample loop in Fig. 2, is used to isolate and inject any of a small number of fixed volumes of sample gas into the carrier gas stream.

careful lubrication to ensure that they do not leak, particularly under vacuum. Some of the taps used with the type of by-pass system shown in Figs. 2, 3, and 4 can be replaced with four-way taps as shown in Fig. 5, or with six-way taps (generally called multiport valves) as shown in Fig. 6. Valves of this or similar design, but made of metal can be fitted to most commercial gas chromatographs. They are difficult to construct in a laboratory unless adequate workshop facilities are available. The essential difficulties remain, namely the need for pressure measurement and for volume calibration.

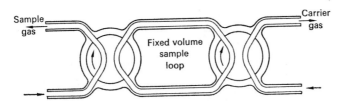

FIG. 5. Four-way taps used for sample injection.

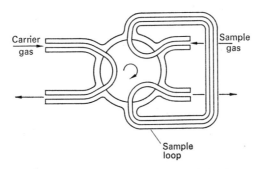

FIG. 6. A six-way tap for sample injection.

Valves that are based upon this multiport principle have been described by Timms *et al.* [4], Haraldson and Thorneman [5], and by Pratt and Purnell [6]. This latter design, shown in Fig. 7 consists of a barrel and key made of stainless steel. The key has six grooves, each containing a silicone rubber O-ring. Four of these grooves are sloping, producing what are effectively four on–off valves. The passage of gas from one port to another is through the annular space between the rings.

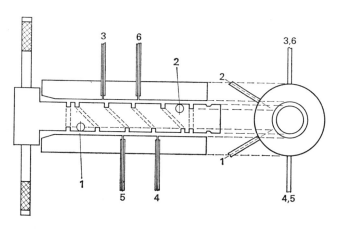

FIG. 7. A multiport sample valve (Pratt and Purnell, *Analyt. Chem.* **32**, 1213, (1960)). 1, vacuum; 2, reaction vessel; 3, 4, sample volume; 5, carrier gas supply; 6, chromatographic column.

Syringe Injection into a Sampling Loop

The advantages of the constant volume pipette may be combined with the simplicity and ease of operation of the syringe injection method, by injecting the sample into a by-pass loop where the pressure has been reduced to atmospheric. The actual volume of the sample injected will depend upon the mode of operation of the syringe (for example whether the volume selected can be accurately reproduced and whether or not the plunger is driven down hard against the stop) and the residual gas pressure in the loop. These difficulties can be avoided by using carefully calibrated syringe pipettes such as the Hamilton when fitted with a Chaney adaptor, or Agla with micrometer screw. Leaking pipettes are a common source of error, and from time to time tests should be made to ensure that any pipette that has developed a leak is not used for accurate analysis. In using a syringe pipette, the action should be performed in exactly that same way each time, and the gas pressure in the loop must be carefully reduced to atmospheric before the sample is inserted.

The sampling valve shown in Fig. 8 has been developed [7] to simplify syringe injection into a by-pass loop. It consists of a four-way glass tap, spring loaded, with a sampling loop in the form of a small chamber between two of the ways. The capacity of the chamber is approximately 3 ml, and it is closed with a serum cap. The life of a cap is considerably greater than that of a rubber septum. Only a single tap movement is now required to admit the sample to the chromatograph and, as the loop is at no time full of sample gas, a volume calibration is no longer required. In order to calibrate the detector response, known amounts of prepared standard gas mixtures or aliquots of pure gas, are injected into the chamber. The error arising from the small volume of gas remaining in the needle at a pressure above atmospheric can be neglected, as the volume is small compared with the total

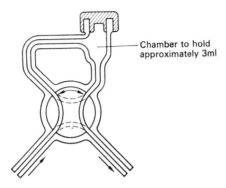

Chamber to hold
approximately 3ml

Fig. 8. A by-pass sample valve for syringe injection (Kipping and Jeffery, *Analyst*, **86**, 680 (1961)).

volume injected, and the determination on any sample is always made under the same conditions as the calibration injections.

Always provided that the sample is introduced in the same way, this method of addition does lead to reproducible chromatographic response. The series of results in Table 1 was obtained by injecting successive 0·5 ml aliquots of air from an Agla

TABLE 1. REPRODUCIBILITY OF THE NITROGEN RESPONSE (SUCCESSIVE INJECTIONS OF 0·5 ml ALIQUOTS OF AIR)

Peak height		
mm	mV	Percentage of mean
194·5	4·168	100·07
194·5	4·168	100·07
194·0	4·157	99·81
194·5	4·168	100·07
194·2	4·161	99·92
194·5	4·168	100·07
Mean 194·37	4·165	100·00

Standard deviation 0·21 mm, 0·005 mV or 0·11%. Recorder sensitivity 5 mV full-scale deflection.

micrometer screw syringe pipette on to a 3 ft length of column packed with molecular sieve No. 5A. The height of the nitrogen peak is recorded as a measure of the chromatographic response.

By-pass injectors similar in principle to that described above can be made of metal. The mating surfaces must, however, be carefully ground and preferably be lubricated, for example with PTFE. Experience has shown that a considerable degree of precision in the machining and finishing of these components is necessary if a leak-proof device is to be obtained.

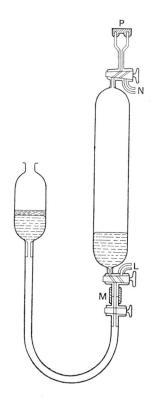

FIG. 9. Gas tube for sample transfer.

Gas samples are usually transferred from the sampling point to the analytical laboratory in gas tubes of about 100 ml capacity with two-way taps at both ends as in Fig. 9 [8]. Aliquots of the gaseous mixtures contained in these tubes can readily be obtained by using the serum cap device and by putting the gas under a slight pressure from a head of mercury. The residual air in the extraction chamber P is removed by evacuation via the arm N, prior to filling with the gas sample from the body of the tube. The gas-tight syringe pipette used to transfer aliquots of the sample to the chromatograph should be purged at least twice with the sample to remove all air from the barrel and needle of the pipette.

As an alternative to the gas tube illustrated, the serum cap can be fitted directly to the chamber such that the hypodermic needle can be inserted into the main bulk of the sample gas. These tubes can also be used for the preparation of simple standard mixtures by injecting known amounts of the trace constituents into the gas tube previously filled with the major component of the required mixture.

Automatic Sample Injectors

With the increasing use of gas chromatography for process control analysis, considerable effort has been devoted to the design and construction of sample valves that can be operated automatically or be activated from remote positions. The requirements for these devices are:

1. They must have low gas-leakage rates.
2. They must be reliable, i.e. operate faultlessly over long periods of time.
3. They must operate positively and deliver the selected gas volume quickly and precisely.
4. They should not give rise to contamination by desorption or loss by adsorption of the sample on the valve material.

Very few "home-made" devices meet these requirements, particularly in respect of low leakage rates and faultless operation. Some commercially available sample valves have similarly been criticized, and no device of this kind should be installed without a thorough testing.

Most commercially available sample valves are designed to be operated both manually and automatically: in this context the latter may be electrical, electro-magnetic, electromechanical (i.e. using cams or gears) or pneumatic. The choice of system is seldom important, and on the process plant use is usually made of the available power supplies. The sample injectors described in the literature have a great deal in common and there is considerable overlap between the various types. They may conveniently be considered in four groups:

1. Rotating plate valves.
2. Piston valves.
3. Linear sliding valves.
4. Diaphragm valves.

Rotating Plate Valves

These consist of a block, usually of PTFE, other plastic material or plastic-faced metal, but sometimes of metal [5], in the form of a flat disc which rotates relative to two metal plates and between which it is sandwiched. Holes drilled through the PTFE block, or channels scored on its surface are used to provide the necessary connections between the carrier gas supply and the chromatographic column, either directly or via a sample volume. This sample volume may be connected within the block itself or in an external sample loop, to which access is obtained in certain positions of the rotating part of the valve (Fig. 10).

Although the block and its containing plates are kept together by spring action, the valves are seldom completely gas-tight—the sealing often suffering from damage by scoring of the plastic material. For this reason such valves have not been popular, although they function well enough at low gas pressures.

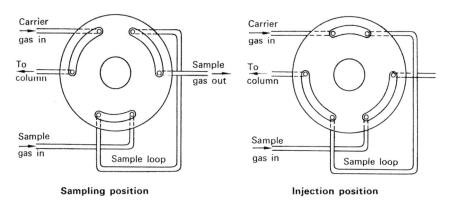

Sampling position   Injection position

Fig. 10. A rotating plate-type sample injector.

Piston Valves

These valves are frequently hollow cylinders with gas connections arranged along the length of the barrel. The piston is usually grooved to take O-rings which act as seals between the piston and the cylinder walls. Typical of such valves is the Aerograph, made with a stainless steel body and fitted with five O-rings, shown in Fig. 11. This particular valve is designed for panel mounting and for both manual and electromagnetic operation. Similar sample injectors are available from Loenco and other manufacturers.

In general piston valves operate satisfactorily at low gas pressures such as those required for most gas chromatographic applications, but frequent replacement of the O-ring seals is necessary if gas-tight operation is to be maintained.

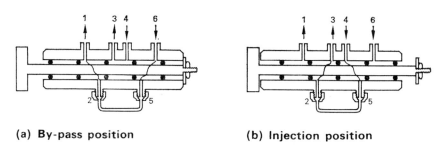

(a) By-pass position   (b) Injection position

Fig. 11. A piston-type sample injector (Varian Aerograph Ltd.).

Linear Sliding Valves (also called "sandwich-type slide valves").

As with rotating plate-type valves, the moving part of the linear sliding valve is often machined from PTFE or PTFE-coated metal to obtain the required degree of surface lubrication. In its simplest form the sample volume is contained within the width of the slide, and this part is transferred from sample gas stream to carrier gas stream (Fig. 12) [9]. Where the sample volume is external to the valve itself, a six-port valve is required. A number of such designs are available commercially, some of which are also available in eight-port and sixteen-port versions which permit of back-flushing of the column.

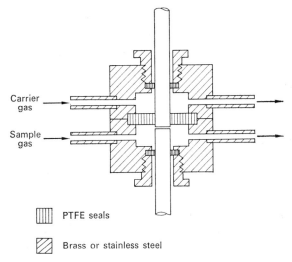

Carrier gas

Sample gas

|||| PTFE seals

//// Brass or stainless steel

FIG. 12. A linear slide-type sample injector (Peterson and Lundberg, *Analyt. Chem.* **33**, 653 (1961)).

The linear slide is probably the most widely used of all types of automatic sample valve, largely because it is cheaper to produce than other types (it is still expensive!), it can be operated at higher gas pressures and remain leak-proof, and its simple operating mechanism is less liable to mechanical failure than that of other types. Most commercially available linear slide valves are operated pneumatically.

Diaphragm Valves

These are usually six-port valves in which the ports are covered by a plastic diaphragm, and are actuated by compressed air [10] or by being attached to a series of pistons which are pneumatically or cam operated (Fig. 13) [11]. This diaphragm allows the ports to be connected in pairs. Operating the valve makes the alternative set of connections in pairs.

A variety of materials have been suggested for the diaphragm including Mylar, polyethylene, polyvinylchloride, polyurethane and PTFE [12]. Difficulties occur in making gas-tight seals with some materials and all absorb certain gas (especially hydrocarbon gases) to some extent. PTFE appears to be one of the better materials.

As with all sample injectors containing metal parts, stainless steel is the preferred material. If the valves are to be used for corrosive gases, then monel metal, hastelloy or other nickel-based alloy should be used.

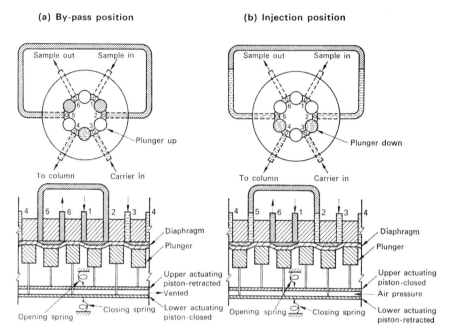

FIG. 13. A diaphragm-type sample injector (Pine, *Talanta*, **14**, 277 (1962)).

Although this type of valve can be made to function without leaks, small scratches on the mating surfaces impair the performance, as do particles of metal, dust, etc., from the gas supplies, which tend to lodge between the diaphragm and the metal surfaces. Where these valves are used, gas filters should be fitted to both carrier gas and sample gas streams.

Miscellaneous Methods

Liquid Nitrogen Traps

These are frequently used to transfer small amounts of condensable gases to a gas chromatograph. One such trap, shown in Fig. 14, is based upon the design of Glew and Young [13]. This consists of a U-tube that can be isolated from the carrier gas flow system by rotating the spring-loaded stopcock through 180°, to the position shown in the figure. The flow of carrier gas is then from *A*, through one hole in the hollow key of the tap, out through the second hole and to the chromatographic column at *B*. The sampling line is attached at *E*, and the sample condensed in the U-tube which is immersed in liquid nitrogen. This sample, isolated from the sampling line, is warmed to room temperature and transferred to the column by rotating the stopcock once more. To prevent the build up of excessive pressures when large gas samples are condensed, the U-tube can be exchanged for a tube of larger size, attached by means of the ball-and-socket joints at positions *C* and *D*.

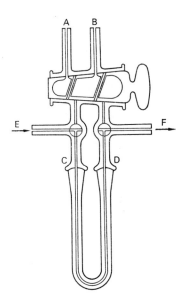

FIG. 14. A liquid nitrogen trap (after Glew and Young, *Analyt. Chem.* **30,** 1890 (1958)).

It is not always convenient to attach such devices permanently to a chromatograph, and for occasional use a simple transfer cell designed by Russell and Bednas [14] is shown in Fig. 15. This consists of two spring-loaded stopcocks, and a hypodermic needle cemented as shown. One arm of the double connection is cooled with liquid nitrogen. The sample is condensed in this arm, allowed to return to room temperature, and then transferred to the chromatograph through a serum cap by means of an additional temporary carrier gas supply connected at *G*.

A simpler version of this trap, also due to Bednas, is shown in Fig. 16. It utilizes a single vacuum stopcock which is evacuated via the hypodermic needle inserted through the serum cap. This transfer cell has been used with various samples and with pressures from vacuum to 30 lb/in².

Generation of the Gas Sample *in situ*

In certain cases it is possible to generate the gas sample in the gas chromatograph, for example carbon dioxide can be liberated from limestone by the action of phosphoric acid, the reaction taking place inside a small reactor permanently attached to a gas chromatograph [15]. In this example the detector response may conveniently be calibrated by the same procedure, but using pure calcium carbonate.

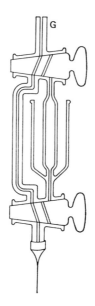

FIG. 15. Sample transfer cell with liquid nitrogen trap (Russell and Bednas, *Analyt. Chem.* **29**, 1562 (1957)).

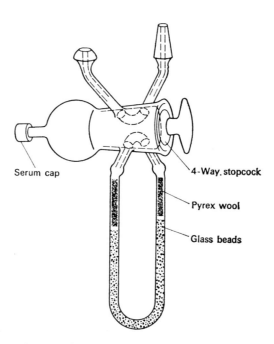

FIG. 16. Gas transfer cell (Bednas, personal communication).

Concentration on an Inert Adsorbent

Certain particular components can be removed from a stream of carrier gas by adsorption on an inert material such as activated charcoal. These components can then be released—generally by heating—in a desorption chamber attached to a gas chromatograph. Large volumes of sample mixture can be taken, enabling quite small concentrations to be determined. This technique has been used for sulphur dioxide [16], where the considerable concentration effected is combined with separation from oxygen which would otherwise interfere in the subsequent chromatographic separation.

Small Quantities of Sample Mixture

When the gas sample consists of only a very small volume, all of which must be used for the analysis, great care must be taken to ensure that no dilution of the sample occurs. Vacuum techniques, as for example, that described by Wilkinson and Hall [17], are commonly used for the measurement and transfer of such samples, but a somewhat simpler method is to use a hypodermic needle attached to a length of precision bore capillary tubing. The tube and needle are filled with a suitable viscous liquid in which none of the components of the sample mixture are soluble—liquid paraffin can be used for many mixtures—and the sample gently sucked into the tube through the needle. The length of the tube occupied by the gas can now be used as a measure of the quantity present. The sample is transferred to the gas chromatograph by inserting the needle through a serum cap into a by-pass sampling loop fitted with a suitable trap to retain the viscous liquid.

Addition of Small Aliquots

The accuracy obtained with a syringe injection decreases as the size of the aliquot is reduced, partly because of the difficulty in measuring the aliquot, and partly

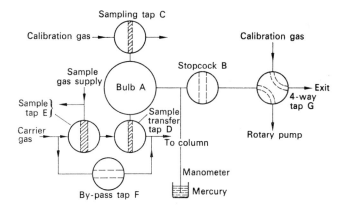

Fig. 17. Gas handling system for the transfer of small amounts of sample material (Berry, *Proc. 4th Symp. Gas Chromatog.*, Hamburg, 1962).

because needle volume and leakage errors are much greater in relation to the smaller volumes taken. A gas handling system designed to transfer quantities of as little as 10^{-5} ml of the sample gas, has been described by Berry [18], and is shown in Fig. 17.

The volume of bulb A is approximately 100 ml; it can be evacuated to a pressure of a few microns of mercury by a two-stage rotary pump via the stopcock B and the four-way tap G. The sample or the gas used for calibration is allowed to flow through the tap C to atmosphere. When the barrel is turned through 90°, the volume of the trapped portion, i.e. 30 μl, is transferred into bulb A. In this way the size of the sample transferred to the column is dependent upon the number of additions made by turning tap C. The bore of the tap D also has a volume of 30 μl, which effectively transfers 0·008 μl of sample per turn of tap C. Alternatively, the pressure in bulb A can be set at any value up to atmospheric by introduction of gas through the tap G. Tap E has a wider bore than taps C and D, and is used only for the addition of much larger aliquots.

The sampling system is appropriate only for use with sensitive detectors, such as the helium ionization detector for which it was designed.

CHAPTER 3

Chromatographic Separation

THE separation of gases upon columns of suitable adsorbent material is seldom a simple single process. Physical adsorption to form a surface monolayer is one of the commonest adsorption processes encountered, but multilayer formation, capillary condensation and chemisorption are often likely to be contributing processes.

The majority of separations made in gas chromatography use liquid stationary phases dispersed upon inert supports. For such separations the adsorption isotherms are generally close to ideal (Fig. 18a) and symmetrical chromatographic peaks are obtained.

The type of adsorption that gives isotherms similar to that shown in Fig. 18c is not often encountered, but is easily identified by the shape of the chromatographic peak which has a sharp tailing edge and a trailing front. An example of this is the adsorption of water on columns packed with activated charcoal; mathematical analysis of a series of such chromatograms has proved a satisfactory method for determining the isotherm [19].

The majority of separations required for the analysis of gaseous mixtures use solid adsorbents, for which the isotherms are generally of the Langmuir type (Fig. 18b). The chromatographic peaks have sharp fronts with trailing backs, although not always as asymmetric as that shown in the figure. For this type of peak the response calibration is seldom linear, and the retention time and volume of the substance will increase as smaller quantities of material are added. This effect is not usually very marked, although in some cases it can be quite exceptional. A particular example of this is the adsorption of nitric oxide on columns packed with molecular sieve No. 5A.

Only a small number of adsorbents are commonly used for gas–solid chromatography and this chapter is devoted to a description of these commonly used materials—silica gel, charcoal, alumina, molecular sieves and porous polymer beads (e.g. "Porapak"). In addition, the use of liquids as stationary phases in gas analysis is also considered for packed and capillary columns. The use of narrow bore, sometimes referred to as packed-capillary columns, is also recorded.

Glass columns have been extensively used for chromatography, they possess the disadvantage that once they are packed they are impossible to coil. Attempts to pack glass columns that are already coiled are rarely successful, owing to the difficulties of avoiding air spaces within the packing and of obtaining a uniform

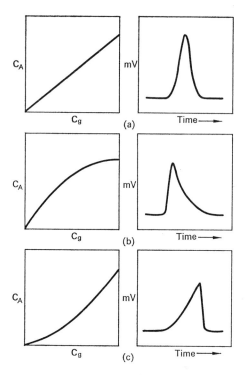

FIG. 18. Absorption isotherms and chromatographic peaks. C_A, concentration of material in solid or liquid phase; C_g, concentration of material in gaseous phase.

packing density over its entire length. When it is necessary to use glass columns, as for example when reactive or corrosive gases are present, a number of straight lengths can be joined as in Fig. 19 prior to packing.

Metal tubing, usually brass or copper, has also been used extensively for chromatographic columns. No difficulty is experienced in packing or coiling brass tubing, but copper tubes should be softened by heating to a temperature of 500–600°, as described by Keulemans [20]. After cooling, the copper tube can be packed and coiled—either by hand or on a lathe—and will harden again during the coiling process. Metal columns are usually joined to the remaining parts of the carrier gas-flow system with compression couplings.

Brass or copper columns cannot be used if the gas mixtures for analysis contain reactive components such as hydrogen sulphide or nitric oxide. For these either glass or aluminium metal columns are preferred. For corrosive gases such as chlorine or hydrogen chloride, only columns of glass or nickel-based alloy should be used.

The carefully prepared stationary phase, activated if necessary, is packed into the selected column using a small vibrator to ensure a constant packing density. A simple device for this can be made from a small electric motor, with a flat surface cut along part of the exposed spindle; this is held against the outside of the column.

This vibrator can be used with metal columns and also, if care is taken, with columns made of glass. When the spindle of the vibrator is first applied to the column, the column material packs down fairly rapidly to give a chromatographic column with the even porous structure required. Further vibration results in packing to a higher density, which increases the pressure drop across the column with consequent decrease of separation efficiency. The packing density required can usually be achieved with a little practice.

FIG. 19. A glass chromatographic column. Long lengths of column can be produced by joining a number of smaller lengths.

The formation of air pockets within the column should be avoided. For this reason, the coiling of a metal tube must be done gradually and with as large a diameter as possible. Where space permits, a minimum diameter of 10 cm and preferably 15 cm should be employed. The column should also be mounted with the axis of the helix in a horizontal rather than a vertical position.

To obtain the most efficient use of a chromatographic column, the minimum quantity of the gaseous sample should be taken, and the carrier gas-flow rate should be as high as possible—provided always that the separation of the components of the mixture is complete. The effect of increasing the flow rate of argon carrier gas through a column packed with molecular sieve No. 5A, upon the resolution of the chromatographic peaks from a sample of towns' gas is shown in Fig. 20. These separations were all made at a temperature of 35°, and could all have been further improved by operating at a lower temperature.

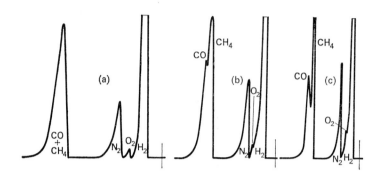

FIG. 20. Effect of increasing the carrier gas flow rate upon the separation of the components of towns' gas. Column: 3-ft molecular sieve No. 5A and 7·5-ft charcoal; temperature, 35°; carrier gas, argon at (a) 10 psi, (b) 15 psi, (c) 20 psi; gas density balance detector.

Gas–Solid Chromatography

Solid adsorbents used as stationary phases in gas–solid chromatography suffer in some degree from a common fault—a steady deterioration in reactivity, and hence a progressive decline in the ability to separate the components of a mixture. The main cause of this deterioration is the irreversible adsorption of one or more compound on the column packing. Examples of this type of adsorption are water on columns of silica gel and both water and carbon dioxide on molecular sieve. In neither case can these components be removed at room temperatures by back flushing, a technique commonly used in gas–liquid chromatography to remove sample components with long retention times from chromatographic columns. To remove this adsorbed water and carbon dioxide from these columns, and to re-activate the packing material, a higher temperature is necessary.

Only five materials have been extensively used as column packings in gas–solid chromatography, namely silica gel, charcoal, alumina, molecular sieves and porous polymer beads. This contrasts with gas–liquid chromatography for which a very large number of stationary phases have been described.

Silica Gel

The ability of a column of silica gel to separate any two components of a gaseous mixture will depend very largely upon the method used in its preparation. For this reason it is almost impossible to reproduce retention times from one column to the next. In order to activate silica gel, it is dried in a vacuum oven at a temperature of about 150°, or in air at a temperature of between 200° and 300°. For most applications the dried material is used, but for some purposes a controlled amount of deactivation has been recommended. This is carried out by adding small, known amounts of either water or a non-volatile organic compound to the dried material. The use of organic compounds for this purpose has been studied by Rossi *et al.* [21], who concluded that the best results for the separation of gaseous hydrocarbons were obtained using silica to which small quantities of benzyl alcohol had been added. The influence of the grade of silica gel used upon the gas separation obtained has been studied by Friedrich [22], and it is clear that once a particular supply of silica gel has been found to be suitable for a given application, then that supply should not lightly be changed.

The importance of consistency in all aspects of activation and deactivation cannot be over-stressed. As with all solid adsorbents, silica gel should not be used unsized, and a fraction in the size range −44 to +100 mesh is probably the most suitable for general work.

Charcoal

Grades of charcoal suitable for gas chromatography are usually sold as such, and are often described as "coconut" or "activated" charcoal. To some extent this latter term is misleading, as further treatment is required before these materials are in a sufficiently active state for gas chromatography. The usual way of obtaining this active state is to heat the appropriate size fraction (usually in the range of −44 to +100 mesh) in a vacuum oven at a temperature of about 150° for a few hours. As with silica gel, material from different sources may have greatly differing properties, and it is therefore advisable to keep to one source of supply, once this has proved to be satisfactory.

The shape of the chromatographic peaks obtained from columns packed with charcoal can often be improved by increasing the temperature at which the column is operating. This unfortunately, also has the effect of reducing the adsorptivity of the packing, and hence the degree of separation possible for any two gaseous components. It is usually possible to effect a compromise.

Alumina

Alumina has been used extensively in gas chromatography for the separation of the hydrocarbon gases. When used in a freshly activated form, the peaks that are obtained tail very badly and have high retention volumes. Scott [23] and Hewett [24] independently showed that this tailing of peaks could be avoided, and faster analyses obtained by deactivating the alumina. Scott first carefully dried his alumina, removing the adsorbed water, and activating the sites available on the material for hydrocarbon adsorption. He then deactivated the alumina by adding water, and showed that the amount of water required to reach minimum polarity was equivalent to that required to form a monolayer on the surface of the solid adsorbent, and that any additional water caused the polarity (and hence tailing) of the material to increase again. He also recorded the beneficial effect of adding a small quantity of silicone oil to the alumina. This addition gave a small ionizing effect which helped to separate some of the otherwise nearly coincident peaks.

Hewett also removed the adsorbed water and activated the alumina by careful drying, but deactivated the material by adding 4% of liquid paraffin. This also had a small ionizing effect which assisted the resolution of the chromatographic peaks. All paraffin and olefin hydrocarbons from C_1 to C_4 are completely separated from each other on columns prepared in this way, with the single exception of isobutene and but-*trans*-2-ene which appear as a single chromatographic peak.

A size fraction of alumina suitable for gas chromatography can be obtained from most chemical supply houses and also from the manufacturers and retailers of chromatographic equipment.

Molecular Sieves

The words "molecular sieve" constitute a trade name for a number of artificially prepared zeolites. They can be obtained from most chemical supply houses in pellet form, and from manufacturers of gas chromatographic equipment in the form of sized fractions. These materials are the only commonly used chromatographic packings that will separate oxygen from nitrogen at room temperatures; for this reason their application to gas analysis has been extensively studied. Since it is possible to use molecular sieves to separate mixtures of hydrogen, oxygen, nitrogen, methane and carbon monoxide, they can be used to obtain the greatest amount of information following a single injection, for a wide variety of gaseous mixtures. Examples of such mixtures include towns' gas, water gas, coal gas, exhaust gases, mine gases and furnace gases.

At room temperatures, carbon dioxide is completely adsorbed on most molecular sieves and cannot be removed by back flushing. This, together with the adsorption of water, results in a slow, steady deterioration of the column, which is usually observed as a progressive loss of the ability to separate oxygen from nitrogen. It is possible to elute carbon dioxide from columns packed with these sieves at elevated temperatures, and a method has been described for determining this gas using temperature programming of the column [25].

A number of molecular sieves is available, but only a few of these are in common use. Of these No. 5A is the one that has been most frequently used as a stationary phase for gas analysis by gas chromatography. Number 3A will pass all molecules with an effective diameter greater than 3Å and (unlike the remaining types) does not therefore absorb carbon dioxide.

TABLE 2. COMMONLY AVAILABLE MOLECULAR SIEVES

Type no.	Molecular sieve	Effective pore diameter
3A	Potassium aluminium silicate	3 Å
4A	Sodium aluminium silicate	4 Å
5A	Calcium aluminium silicate	5 Å
13X	Sodium aluminium silicate	10 Å

Fresh material is usually activated by heating at a temperature of 350–400°, for a period of about 2 hr. Column packings that have deteriorated to the point where they will no longer separate oxygen from nitrogen, can be restored almost to their previous active state by placing the columns in an oven, and heating at this temperature for a period of 1 hr with argon gas flowing through. In practice, it is often found to be more convenient to repack such columns with freshly activated new material rather than attempt to regenerate the previous active condition.

For a given volume of sample, the critical separation upon a column packed with molecular sieve—that of oxygen from hydrogen—increases with increase of column diameter (Fig. 21). This figure shows clearly that there is an optimum carrier gas flow rate for this separation.

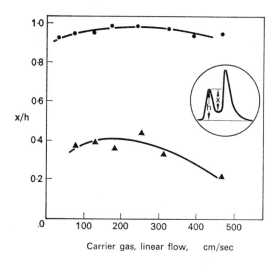

FIG. 21. The separation of oxygen from hydrogen with change of carrier gas flow rate; column—molecular sieve No. 5A. Upper curve—1/4 in. diam. column, lower curve—3/16 in. diam. column.

With the larger diameter columns the increase in separation is accompanied by a decrease in sensitivity which is of particular concern when the gaseous mixture contains carbon monoxide. The peak height sensitivity to carbon monoxide can, however, be improved slightly by lowering the flow rate of gas through the column. This results in a longer residence time on the column, and the best compromise appears to be in the region of 200 cm/sec, equivalent to a pressure drop of 10–12 lb/in² across a 6 ft length of column packed with molecular sieve ground to −52, +72 mesh size.

The efficiency of columns packed with molecular sieves expressed in terms of the number of theoretical plates, also depends upon the carrier gas flow rate. The maximum efficiency is obtained at about 200 cm/sec for both nitrogen (Fig. 22) and methane. For carbon monoxide a not very pronounced maximum was observed at 300 cm/sec, and for hydrogen no maximum at linear gas velocities of up to 400 cm/sec.

All the components of the gaseous mixtures commonly separated on columns packed with molecular sieve, that is hydrogen, oxygen, nitrogen, methane and carbon monoxide, show an increased sensitivity determined by peak height measurement at low linear flow rates, with maxima observed or indicated near the lowest linear velocities studied.

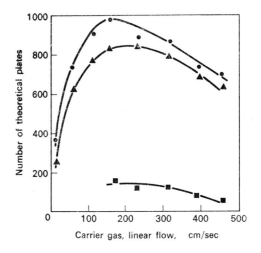

FIG. 22. Efficiency of columns packed with molecular sieve in the determination of nitrogen with change of carrier gas flow rate for ●–● 1/4 in., ▲–▲ 3/16 in., and ■–■ 1/8 in. columns.

Column temperature. The ability of a column packed with molecular sieve to separate oxygen from nitrogen decreases with increase of column temperature. For most purposes the best temperature to use is the lowest at which a heat-input thermostat mechanism can be employed. For particular applications, for example the separation of argon from oxygen, temperatures considerably below ambient have been used.

Column length. For routine analysis of gases containing hydrogen as the major constituent, the critical separation on columns packed with molecular sieve is that of oxygen from hydrogen. Acceptable separation of these components in such mixtures as coal gas, towns' gas or water gas, cannot be achieved on columns of less than about 150 cm (5 ft), unless the carrier gas velocity is reduced to less than 100 cm/sec. This rate is not normally acceptable because of the long residence time of carbon monoxide. With a 150 cm length of column, good separations of oxygen from hydrogen have been obtained at linear velocities of up to 400 cm/sec.

Particle size. With a given size of sample aliquot, and constant physical dimensions of the chromatographic column, the separation of oxygen from hydrogen is improved slightly as the average particle size of the molecular sieve is decreased. This improvement in separation is not sufficient to compensate for the very large increase in the retention times of all the components. Little change of sensitivity as determined by peak height or peak area measurement has been noted with change of particle size. It does not appear to be worth while using small-sized material with the resultant increase of pressure differential across the column if a conventional thermal conductivity detector is used. However, smaller sized material, shorter columns and reduced size of the sample aliquot can be used in conjunction with a micro-thermal conductivity cell or other sensitive detector. For normal use, a convenient size of molecular sieve material was found to be that passing a 52 mesh, but retained on a 72 mesh sieve. The use of molecular sieve flour on Chromosorb inert support has, however, been reported to give an increase in sensitivity and also improved resolution (see p. 103).

In addition to its use in the analysis of gaseous mixtures containing hydrogen, oxygen, nitrogen, methane and carbon monoxide, molecular sieves possess an ability to absorb straight-chain hydrocarbons (methane excepted), which enables it to be used for a separation of the normal hydrocarbons from those with branched chains, which are separated and eluted from molecular sieve material. This separation cannot readily be obtained in any other way.

Porous Polymer Beads

One of the greatest advances in stationary phases was the introduction of the porous polymer beads developed by Hollis [26]. These are now marketed under the name "Porapak". A number of types, designated by the letters P, Q, R, S and T are available: these have surfaces modified by the addition of polar monomers to the basic polymeric material to give different retention characteristics, such as relative retention times. For example, water is eluted just after ethane from Porapak Q, and its retention is moved progressively in time until it is eluted with the butanes from Porapak T.

These materials have a number of very significant advantages over other packing materials, notably the elution of polar compounds with sharp, symmetrical peaks. They have found their greatest use as replacements for certain liquid phases in gas–liquid chromatography, most of which is outside the scope of this book. However, the property of giving near linear adsorption isotherms for polar compounds has made them indispensable in the chromatographic separation of such compounds as water, sulphur dioxide and hydrogen sulphide. They are stable up to 250° (Porapak T up to 200°), are easily and reproducibly packed into the column and have a very rapid recovery from over-load. If required, they can be modified by coating with a liquid stationary phase. They were probably used for the analysis of the Martian Atmosphere [27], as in addition to the above advantages they do not deteriorate when subjected to vacuum or radiation. The chromatogram (Fig. 23), shows the separation of possible constituents of Martian atmosphere using an 8 ft column 0·1 in. internal diameter packed with 50–80 mesh Porapak Q in series in the column of identical dimensions packed with Porapak R and temperature programmed from 25° to 150° at 12° per min.

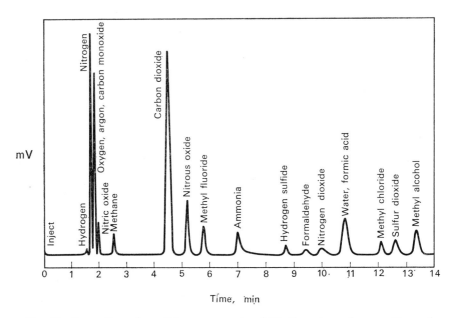

FIG. 23. Separation of possible components of Martian atmosphere on Porapak Q/Porapak R column (Wilhite and Hollis, *J. Gas Chromatog.* **6,** 84 (1968)).

Gas–Liquid Chromatography

Packed Partition Columns

When the components of a gaseous mixture have different solubilities in some non-volatile liquid, then partition or gas–liquid chromatography may be used to separate the mixture into its several components. Wherever it is possible to use this type of chromatography it is preferable to do so, as the columns, unlike those used in gas–solid chromatography, do not usually deteriorate in use. This is because irreversible adsorption seldom occurs, and any components with long residence times that are not eluted in the usual way can be removed by back flushing the column. The main cause of any deterioration of partition columns is loss of the stationary phase. This can occur through making a poor selection from the liquid phases that are now available, or more commonly by operating the column at too high a temperature. Some liquid phases that have been reported for the separation of gaseous compounds are given in Table 3.

The liquid stationary phase is evenly dispersed over the surface of an inert solid known as the support material—celite or firebrick being commonly used. This dispersion is usually achieved by dissolving the selected liquid phase in a suitable solvent, often methanol or acetone, and stirring it into the support material to form a slurry. The solvent is then evaporated while the mixture is stirred continuously. The amount of liquid phase, relative to the solid support, has varied in the range 5–45%. The small percentages are used in conjunction with ionization detectors which require only very small sample aliquots.

TABLE 3. SOME STATIONARY PHASES USED FOR GAS ANALYSIS

Liquid phase	Determination	Reference
Dinonylphthalate	SO_2	28
Tritolylphosphate	SO_2, H_2S	29, 30
Silicone grease	H_2S	31
Dimethyl sulphoxide	O_2, N_2O, CO_2	32
Dimethyl sulpholane	Hydrocarbons	33, 34
Hexamethylphosphoramide	CO_2	35
Glycerol with silver nitrate	Unsaturated Hydrocarbons	36
Ethylene glycol with silver nitrate	Unsaturated Hydrocarbons	37

Even the most inactive solid support often does contribute a small adsorptive effect to the partition between liquid and gas. The effect is usually encountered or noticed only when the smaller amounts of liquid phase are dispersed on the solid support. Some improvement can generally be obtained by treating this support with a silicone solution. Materials such as celite or firebrick are commercially available in suitable size grades, acid and alkali washed, and silane treated, in the range 40–150 mesh. Of these fractions 80–100 mesh and 100–120 mesh are those most commonly used for gas chromatography.

High column efficiencies are obtained with fine particle size of the support material coupled with low pressure drop across the column or more correctly with low values for the ratio of gas pressure at the inlet of the column (p_i) to that at the outlet (p_o). As with solid adsorbents, these conditions cannot be varied independently, and a compromise must be effected. Unsized ground material should not be used as a chromatographic support, as it invariably leads to a very much higher pressure drop across the column than when the appropriate size fraction is used, and hence to an increase of the ratio p_i/p_o.

The packing technique used for filling columns with solid adsorbents can also be used to pack the solid support containing the liquid phase, as these are or should be apparently dry and free-running.

Gas–liquid chromatography is extensively used for the analysis of liquid and volatile solid samples, and in the field of gas analysis has been applied to the determination of the hydrocarbon gases and gases with appreciable polarity such as sulphur dioxide, hydrogen sulphide and carbon dioxide.

Capillary Columns

Capillary columns are a particular application of gas–liquid chromatography in which open narrow-bore tubes are coated with a thin film of the liquid phase. The pressure drop across such columns is very small, with ratios p_i/p_o approaching unity, giving high efficiencies. Columns of this type suggested by Martin [38] and developed by Golay [39] are sometimes referred to as Golay columns. Column lengths of a few hundred feet are by no means uncommon.

The internal walls of the metal, glass or nylon capillary tube of about 0·01 in.

(0·2–0·3 mm) internal diameter, are coated with a partitioning liquid by first filling the tube with a 5–10% solution of the stationary phase in a suitable solvent. A pressure of about 3 lb/in² is used to force the solution into and through the tube. The ideal rate of travel of solution through the tube is about 10 cm/sec. Once the tube is completely filled, the source of the solution is removed, and sufficient pressure is maintained to evaporate the solvent and so leave a thin layer of stationary phase on the internal walls of the capillary. Care should be taken that as the tube empties the rate of travel of the remaining solution through the tube does not increase to any appreciable extent. As only a very small amount of stationary phase is left in the column, only very small quantities of the gaseous sample mixtures can be taken for analysis. As a result of the high linear velocity of carrier gas through open tubing and the low pressure drop across such columns, extremely long column lengths can be used, facilitating difficult separations. Alternatively, by using high carrier gas pressure at the column inlet, very rapid separations can be obtained, although the high efficiencies normally obtained with such columns are thereby sacrificed. It is this application that is of interest in the field of gas analysis, chiefly for the separation of gaseous hydrocarbon mixtures.

In order to use capillary columns, a very sensitive detection system is required, together with a means of adding a small enough quantity of the mixture for analysis, as a plug at the head of the column. Lovelock [40] and McWilliam and Dewar [41] have provided the analyst with two very sensitive detectors suitable for this application, but micro-thermal conductivity cells are probably more useful for the analysis of mixtures of the permanent gases on a routine basis.

The introduction of a small enough sample is usually achieved by inserting a simple stream-splitter in the form of a T-piece between the front of the column and the injection device (usually a serum cap or septum) so that only a small proportion of the sample injected is swept on to the column. The remainder, amounting to 95% or more of the sample is allowed to escape. It should be noted that for maximum column efficiency the sample should be added directly to the top of the column, ensuring plug flow through the column.

For high speed analysis, the capillary column together with an appropriate detector should be coupled to a recording system with a very fast response time. For this Scott and Cumming [42] have used a cathode ray tube with a long persistence screen.

Narrow-bore packed partition columns, scaled down in size from columns of the conventional dimensions, are also used for high speed analysis, and this use is likely to be extended to the field of process control analysis. The equivalent of a capillary column using gas–solid chromatography has been described by Mohnke and Saffert [43], and used for the separation of hydrogen isotopes at a temperature of −196°. This column was prepared by filling a glass capillary with a 17% solution of ammonia, which was then sealed at both ends and heated for 70 hours at a temperature of 170°. At the end of this period the capillary was opened and the ammonia solution removed. The temperature was then raised slowly to 190° with air passing through the tube until completely dry. This treatment gave a glass capillary with a thin layer of active silica on the inner wall.

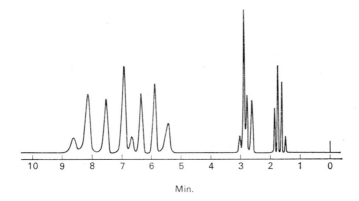

FIG. 24. Separation of hydrocarbons on graphitized carbon black (Schneider and Bruderreck, *Analyt. Chem.* **36**, 1535 (1964)).

A somewhat simpler technique for obtaining this thin layer of active silica was described by Schwartz *et al.* [44]. Silica in the form of a colloidal solution in a water–isopropanol mixture was evaporated onto the inner walls of plastic or metal capillaries, which were then purged with dry argon to remove the solvent. Sharp peaks were obtained using these columns for the separation of hydrocarbon mixtures. Little trailing was observed, and a separation was obtained in the carbon number range C_1 to C_7. Molecular sieves have been deposited on the walls of narrow bore tubing (0·04 in.) by Purcell [45] and an active layer of oxide film has been produced on the surface of an aluminium capillary tube by Petitjean and Lefthault [46]. Both these applications gave advantages more usually associated with capillary columns. A graphitized carbon black was produced in a 10 m length of capillary column, modified with 0·4% by weight of squalane by Schneider and Bruderreck [47]. They obtained the hydrocarbon analysis shown in Fig. 24.

CHAPTER 4

Detectors

IN passage through a chromatographic column, the original sample is separated into a number of components which are carried in turn by the stream of carrier gas to the detector. The function of the detector is to indicate or record the presence of these components, preferably by means of a signal, the extent of which is a measure of the quantity of sample or of the concentration of the component present. A large variety of detectors have been described, making use of chemical or physical properties in the sensing mechanism. The detectors that are most widely employed are those in which the signal is in the form of an electrical impulse which can be amplified where necessary before display or recording.

Although some of the detectors described in the first edition are still not widely used, the authors are of the opinion that for certain particular components they still have their application in gas analysis by gas chromatographic methods and they are therefore retained in this second edition.

In the first published experiments in gas chromatography, James and Martin [2] used a titration cell to detect the components of the sample, in their case mixtures of fatty acids. The separated components were absorbed in water and titrated automatically with sodium hydroxide solution. This titration cell detector utilizing the acid–base properties of the sample components, is of low sensitivity, and of very restricted application. In the field of gas analysis its use is limited to the small number of soluble acidic or alkaline gases such as hydrogen chloride, ammonia or methylamine, and these only when present in quantity. In view of these practical limitations as a chromatographic detector, it is not surprising that the titration cell has never been extensively used.

The first detector to achieve widespread popularity was the katharometer or thermal conductivity cell, in which changes of conductivity of the carrier gas stream due to the presence of the sample components are used to produce an electrical signal. The convenience of an electrical output, the wide range of materials to which it responds, its simplicity, stability and sensitivity have undoubtedly been contributing factors to the extensive use of this detector.

Martin and James [48] also invented a device for measuring the density of the gas stream as it emerges from the chromatographic column. This device, known as a gas-density balance has presented considerable problems in manufacture, and it is only in the form of a later development that this detector has passed into common use.

The β-ray ionization detector, now more commonly known as the cross-section ionization detector, introduced by Boer [49], was followed by the flame ionization detector of McWilliam and Dewar [41] and the argon ionization detector of Lovelock [40]. These latter detectors have important applications in the field of gas analysis, although they are more widely known for their use in the detection and determination of organic liquids and volatile solids.

A number of newer detectors have been introduced for particular fields of analysis, but most of these have been derived from or are logical variations of these earlier developments. Not all the detectors that have been described have been brought into common use—the flame emissivity detector [50, 51], for example, although described in several books, has yet to be widely adopted.

Detectors used in gas chromatography may be either integral, in that the response is a function of the total quantity of material, in this case of sample gas, that has passed through it, or differential, in that the response is a function of the gas concentration at any particular time. In the majority of applications it is the quantity or integral response that is required, and where differential detectors are used, some means of integration is often employed.

The titration cell previously noted, is an example of an integral detector, other examples are the Brunel mass integral detector which continuously weighs the accumulation of eluted components, and the nitrometer or gas burette, often referred to as the Janak detector, which continuously records the accumulated volume of the eluted components (after removal of the carbon dioxide used as carrier gas by absorption in aqueous potassium hydroxide solution). Differential detectors are more numerous and examples include the thermal conductivity cell, gas-density balance and the various types of ionization detector.

Integral Detectors

All integral detectors so far developed suffer from two big disadvantages. Firstly, that unless special steps are taken for their isolation, the components of the mixture are not recovered individually but are recombined in the actual detector. Secondly, none of these detectors is very sensitive in the present form. Thus, although they find use in the determination of components present in quantity in any given mixture, they cannot be used for components present in only trace amounts.

Brunel Mass Integral Detector [52]

This detector is unique among the list of detectors in that the response is given directly in units of weight. The detector is made in the form of a small chamber attached to a thermobalance, or in the more recent models, suspended from the arm of an automatically recording electro microbalance [53]. The chamber contains an absorbent material, such as active charcoal, which will retain the components of the sample mixture but not the carrier gas. Where all the components are absorbed, the total weight of the sample can be obtained from the final integral. If the initial sample weight is known, then it is necessary only that the components of interest can be absorbed, weighed and correctly identified.

This detector was developed by Thorburn and his co-workers at Brunel College, and although its application to gas analysis is restricted to determining the major components of mixtures where they can readily be absorbed, it should be of widespread application to volatile liquids and solids. Advantages claimed for this detector are that the results are not affected by small changes of column temperature, or of carrier gas flow rate during the course of an experiment. In the more recent development [53], Thorburn and co-workers give a lower limit of detection of 0·5 μg and an upper limit of 25 mg.

Nitrometer, Gas Burette, "Janak Detector"

This detector, first described by Janak [54, 55], requires the use of carbon dioxide as carrier gas. A direct measurement is made of the volume of the eluted components after removal of the carrier gas by absorption in aqueous potassium hydroxide solution. The sample remaining at this stage must therefore be in the gaseous state at the temperature of operation, must not react with the caustic alkali used, and must be present in more than trace amounts. Gases that can be determined by the Janak method include hydrogen, nitrogen, oxygen, carbon monoxide and the hydrocarbons in the range C_1 to C_4 that do not condense under normal working conditions.

Carbon dioxide of high purity is required as carrier gas. This can sometimes be obtained from commercially available gas cylinders, but in practice a number of impurities are often present, and it is necessary to "blow off" a large proportion of the contents of each cylinder to obtain a gas of adequate purity. It is preferable to use solid carbon dioxide contained in a small pressure vessel as the source of the carbon dioxide gas.

The apparatus used for the Janak method is shown in Fig. 25. It consists of an absorption vessel of alkali-resistant glass, connected to a water-jacketed gas burette via the spherical ground glass joint and tube. The outlet from the chromatographic column must feed below the surface of the mercury pool to prevent caustic alkali solution flowing back into the column when the carrier gas ceases to flow.

The carbon dioxide carrier gas is completely absorbed in this vessel, and the separated components of the gaseous sample mixture, insoluble in both the caustic alkali and the brine used in the gas burette are collected in turn. The reservoir containing brine serves as a levelling device, used prior to recording gas volume measurements. The integral chromatogram is obtained by plotting against time the measurements of gas contained in the burette. The height of each step represents the volume of each component, and the total integral the total volume of the sample—excluding carbon dioxide and other soluble gases.

Other Integral Detectors

The example of the titration cell has already been noted. Other examples of integral detectors include a cell for measuring the thermal conductivity of an absorbing solution described by Boer [56] and the constant volume gas burette described by Van de Craats [57] in which gas pressures are measured at constant volume, after removal of the carbon dioxide used as carrier gas by absorption in aqueous alkali, as in the Janak method. The advantage of pressure measurements is that they are easier to record automatically. None of these integral detectors has found much application in the field of gas analysis.

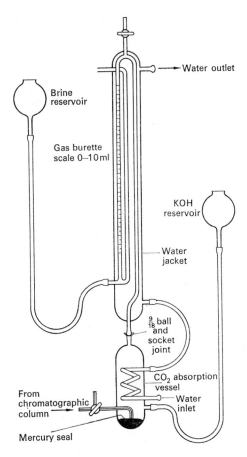

FIG. 25. Apparatus for the Janak methods of analysis (Institute of Petroleum, Standards for Petroleum and its Products).

Differential Detectors

This is by far the most important and most numerous of the two groups of detectors. Those most frequently employed are included in Table 4, which gives also some particular applications within the broad field of gas analysis. These detectors are described in greater detail in this and the next chapter.

These differential detectors are based upon the measurement of some physical property of the separated gaseous components, for example thermal conductivity, density or ionization potential. With the notable exception of the flame detectors in which oxidation occurs, most of these detectors can be used in conjunction with a trapping system to isolate and remove any separated component for subsequent examination by, for example, infrared spectroscopy [58].

TABLE 4. SOME DIFFERENTIAL DETECTORS

Detector	Application
Katharometer (thermal conductivity cell)	Permanent gases
Gas density balance	Permanent gases
Coulometric detectors	Halogens, sulphur
Electrolytic conductivity detector	Halogen, sulphur, nitrogen
Flame detectors	
Flame thermocouple	Hydrocarbon gases
Flame ionization	Hydrocarbon gases
Flame emissivity	Hydrocarbon gases
Flame photometric	Sulphur, phosphorus
Alkali flame ionization	Halogens, sulphur, phosphorus
Other ionization detectors	
Cross-section ionization	Permanent gases
Argon ionization and "helium cell"	NO, NO_2 permanent gases
Electron capture ionization	Halogens
Photo-ionization	Ionizable gases

The introduction of ionization detectors (particularly the more recent development of the flame ionization family which has improved the detection of halogen- and phosphorus-containing compounds) has been one of the major advances in gas chromatography. For many applications these detectors, which are very much more sensitive and in some instances very much more selective, have superseded the older types such as the katharometer. This increased sensitivity permits the use of smaller sized sample aliquots, and hence results in improved resolution. For the determination of the major constituents of permanent gas mixtures, the katharometer is still widely used, and has the advantage of requiring no complex electrical equipment for signal amplification. This advantage is shared with the gas-density balance in its several forms.

Katharometer (Thermal Conductivity Cell)

When a heated metal filament is positioned inside a cavity in a metal block of suitable heat capacity, the temperature attained by the filament will depend largely upon the rate at which the heat from it is conducted across the gas contained in the cavity separating the filament from the metal block. Changes of conductivity of this gas lead to temperature changes of the filament, which give rise to changes of resistance that can be detected and measured.

This principle is used in the construction of the katharometer or thermal conductivity cell, which consists essentially of two passages drilled in a metal block through which the carrier gas is passing. Electrically heated filaments, either two or four in number, are suspended in these passages.

Only pure carrier gas passes through one of the two passages known as the "reference arm". The separated components of the sample mixture are passed, together with the carrier gas, through the second passage known as the "measuring" or "sensing arm". Changes of conductivity occasioned by the passage of a gas other than the carrier gas over the hot wire filament in the measuring arm result in changes of heat dissipation from this filament and therefore in temperature and resistance of the wire. These changes, measured using a Wheatstone bridge network, result in an out-of-balance potential across the bridge, which can conveniently be displayed on a potentiometric recorder.

The magnitude of the response depends upon the thermal conductivity of the separated gases relative to that of the carrier gas and the direction of the response upon whether this thermal conductivity is greater or less than that of the carrier gas. Of the gases commonly used as carrier, argon has a thermal conductivity lower than most other gases, the exceptions being carbon dioxide, sulphur dioxide, chlorine and hydrogen sulphide (Table 5). When using argon as carrier gas, these four materials all have a chromatographic response in the reverse direction to that of the remaining common gases. Hydrogen has a thermal conductivity greater than all the remaining gases, and the response of these gases when hydrogen is used as carrier, is therefore of the same polarity as the response of carbon dioxide, sulphur dioxide, chlorine and hydrogen sulphide when argon is used as carrier gas. Other gases commonly used as carrier with thermal conductivity cells are nitrogen and helium.

TABLE 5. THERMAL CONDUCTIVITIES OF SOME GASES [59]

Gas	Thermal conductivity, cal/cm.sec/deg	
	0°	100°
Acetylene	4·40	
Ammonia	5·135	7·09
Argon	3·88	5·087
Carbon dioxide	3·393	5·06
Carbon monoxide	5·425	
Chlorine	1·829	
Ethane	4·303	7·673
Ethylene	4·02	6·36
Helium	33·60	39·85
Hydrogen	39·60	49·94
Hydrogen sulphide	3·045	
Methane	7·20	
Neon	10·87	
Nitric oxide	5·55	
Nitrogen	5·68	7·18
Nitrous oxide	3·515	5·06
Oxygen	5·70	7·427
Sulphur dioxide	1·950	

One of the first references to the use of katharometers in gas chromatography was by Ray [60], and it was this author in a later publication [61] who showed that it was the greater wire temperature possible when using hydrogen as carrier, that led to greater sensitivity, and not the great difference in thermal conductivity between the carrier gas and the gaseous component being determined.

Many designs of thermal conductivity cell have been described, differing in the metal used for the block, in the method used to mount the filaments, and in the internal geometry of the passages. These designs can conveniently be grouped into three types of which the flow-through type shown in Fig. 26a is the one most commonly used in gas chromatography. In this design, the filaments are placed in such a way that the total flow of gas passes through the passage containing the filaments. This gives the highest sensitivity of the various forms, but also results in undue sensitivity to small changes in carrier gas flow rate. A design that is almost insensitive to change of gas flow, but is also less sensitive to the eluted of gaseous components is the duffusion type of cell shown in Fig. 26b. A compromise between these two designs is the by-pass cell shown in Fig. 26c.

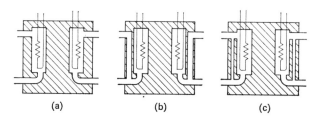

(a)   (b)   (c)

FIG. 26. Types of thermal conductivity cell. (a) Straight through, (b) diffusion, (c) by-pass.

The cells shown in these diagrams are all available commercially. Many users of katharometers prefer to make their own, using brass or stainless steel blocks and platinum wire filaments. In general the sensitivity of such katharometers is not as great as that of the commercial models, and as the sensing volume is greater, the chromatographic peaks tend to be much broader. Some improvement in resolution can often be obtained by reducing the sensing volume, but unless coiled or folded filaments are used, some loss of sensitivity will be incurred, and the overall performance will be inferior to that of a commercial model.

As an alternative to platinum filaments, coiled tungsten wires can be used, in which case the depth of the holes drilled in the block can be reduced considerably. Whatever type of filament is used, and whatever design of cell is chosen, care must be taken to match the filaments as closely as possible. This applies not only to electrical resistance, but to mechanical tension and to the positioning of the wires within the two passageways.

The changes of resistance of these filaments that occur during the passage of separated components through the cell are detected by means of a Wheatstone bridge network. A suitable circuit for a two- or four-filament katharometer is given in Fig. 27. A battery or accumulator can be used to provide the 12 V direct current, but for long-term stability a mains operated power pack is preferred. Provision has been made for continuously varying the bridge current used also to heat the filaments. For many applications in gas analysis these potentiometers can be replaced by fixed resistors, giving a fixed value for the bridge current; this serves to increase the stability of the bridge circuit.

The electrical circuit for a hot wire katharometer can be used also for a thermistor model thermal conductivity cell, with only slight modifications. In these cells the current consumption is very small, and for this reason a dry battery is generally used. In either case, where batteries or accumulators are used, provision must be made for metering and adjusting the current through the hot wires or thermistors. The temperature of operation of thermistor katharometers is usually limited to

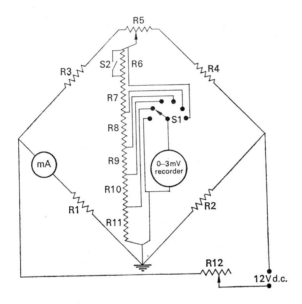

Fig. 27. Circuit diagram of a chromatograph based upon a thermal conductivity cell. *R1–R4*, filaments of cell; *R5*, 10 turn 2-ohm potentiometer; *R6*, 1000-ohm; *R7*, 400-ohm; *R8*, 400-ohm; *R9*, 140-ohm; *R10*, 40-ohm; *R11*, 20-ohm; *R12*, 0–100-ohm.

about 110°. It should be noted that the resistance of thermistors, unlike that of hot wire filaments, decreases with rise in temperature. As thermistor beads are very much smaller than hot wires, the volume of the sensing arm can be reduced considerably, giving rise to a shorter response time and improved resolution. The thermistor model katharometer is about ten times as sensitive as the simple hot wire model.

In view of these clear advantages in the use of thermistors, it must be pointed out that they can only be obtained with a good pair of thermistors. Much time and effort can be wasted in attempts to select matched pairs from a dozen or so apparently identical thermistors. Moreover, continuous operation of thermistors in a current of hydrogen gas results in a rapid deterioration of the bead, and after a short while it becomes impossible to balance the Wheatstone bridge.

For operation at higher temperatures (100–300°), hot wire katharometers are always to be preferred. The major difficulties encountered in working at these temperatures are those of keeping the electrical insulation intact, and the gas flow system leak-proof.

Where corrosive gases are present, katharometers can be constructed from glass. Littlewood et al. [62] have described such a design, in which the gas flow passages, made of glass tubing, are immersed in mercury to give the required heat capacity.

Micro- and semi-micro-katharometers are now available with small cell volumes (down to 3 μl) and whose sensitivities are comparable with that of a flame ionization detector (see following chapter). In this form they can be used in conjunction with capillary columns, and thus find use in the detection of hydrocarbon gases.

A useful variant of an otherwise standard katharometer is that in which the filaments are coated with a palladium catalyst [63]. To the normal response of these filaments to the components passing through the cell must be added the thermal effects of catalytic action—usually hydrogenation. In order to separate the two responses, an identical katharometer with standard filaments is used, connected in series with that used for catalytic conversion. Each cell requires its own Wheatstone bridge circuit, and the outputs from the two bridges, being two separate chromatographic signals, can be displayed on separate recorders, or if well balanced, recorded in opposition on a single chart recorder. In this latter case, only compounds that are hydrogenated will be detected. This detector combination is useful for unsaturated hydrocarbon gases.

Gas-density Balance

There are two types of gas-density balance in use, the design of Martin and James [48], known as the Martin gas-density balance, and the somewhat simpler model made by the Gow-Mac Instrument Company. Both types of gas-density balance use the same principle, that of distributing the gas sample in a vertical passage according to the density of its components. This vertical passage connects two other ways containing or joined by a flow-sensitive device.

This detector in either of its forms, has two advantages over the katharometer, firstly the separated components of the sample mixture do not pass directly over the flow-sensitive elements. This is of particular importance where the sample for analysis contains corrosive gases, or where mixtures containing large quantities of hydrogen are being examined with thermistor beads as the detector elements. And secondly, it is possible to obtain results without undertaking a calibration using pure materials. This is done by equating the sum of the corrected peak areas to 100%. The wt. % of a component n is given by

$$\frac{100 . F_n . A_n}{\Sigma(F_n . A_n)}$$

where A_n is the peak area of the component response, and F_n is the ratio

$$\frac{\text{mol. wt.}_n}{\text{mol. wt.}_n - \text{mol. wt.}_{\text{carrier}}}.$$

The assumption is made that all the components of the sample have been eluted detected and correctly identified.

Hydrogen and helium are not recommended as carrier gases with this detector, argon or nitrogen being preferred. With argon the chromatographic response for most common gases is in the same direction. Exceptions are carbon dioxide, chlorine, nitrous oxide and sulphur dioxide which all have molecular weights, and hence densities greater than that of argon (Table 6). As the response depends directly upon the *difference* in density between the separated components and the carrier gas, some variation in sensitivity can be obtained by appropriate selection of the latter. The greatest response is obtained using sulphur hexafluoride as carrier [64].

TABLE 6. DENSITY OF SOME COMMON GASES [65]

Gas	Density, g/l., 0°, 760 mm
Acetylene	1·173
Ammonia	0·771
Argon	1·784
Carbon dioxide	1·977
Carbon monoxide	1·250
Chlorine	3·214
Ethane	1·357
Ethylene	1·260
Helium	0·178
Hydrogen	0·0899
Hydrogen sulphide	1·539
Methane	0·717
Neon	0·900
Nitric oxide	1·340
Nitrogen	1·251
Nitrous oxide	1·978
Oxygen	1·429
Propane	2·010
Sulphur dioxide	2·927
Sulphur hexafluoride	6·602

Gow-Mac gas-density balance. This balance is in the form of a rectangular metal block containing a number of flow passages. In two of these are the sensing elements which are connected to external resistors to form a Wheatstone bridge circuit. In using the gas-density balance, thermal unbalance of the bridge is produced by changes in the distribution of the flow of carrier over these sensing elements. This gas flow system is shown in a simplified form in Fig. 28. Pure carrier gas enters the balance at E and the gas from the chromatographic column at H. When the gas entering at H is pure carrier gas, the flow divided equally along the passages EF and EG, before passing to the atmosphere at J.

When a gas of greater specific gravity than that of the carrier gas emerges from the chromatographic column and is carried in the stream of carrier gas to the

point H, where the gas flow is at least 25 ml/min less than at *E*, the state of equi-
partition of gas flow in the passages *EF* and *EG* ceases to exist because a density
gradient is set up in the vertical column *FG*, causing more of the gas entering at *H*
to leave via *G* than via the *F* junction. This results in a proportional increase in the

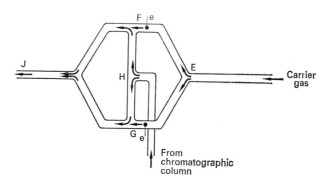

FIG. 28. Gas flow system for a gas-density balance. e, sensing element.

flow of carrier gas from *E* to *F* and a corresponding decrease in the flow from *E* to *G*.
It is this redistribution of the flow of gas in the passages *EF* and *EG* that is detected
and forms the basis of chromatographic response.

This type of gas-density balance is available with either hot wire or thermistor
sensing elements, the latter being the more sensitive. The circuit diagram of a gas

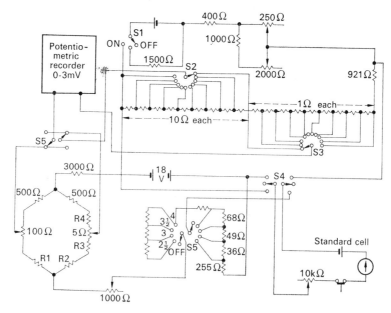

FIG. 29. Circuit diagram of a chromatograph based upon a thermistor model
gas density vs. balance. *R1*, *R2*, thermistor beads; *R3*, *R4* balancing resistors,
about 50 ohms each.

chromatograph built for the purpose of undertaking gas analyses using a thermistor model gas-density balance is shown in Fig. 29. It does not incorporate means of continuously varying the bridge current, but a choice of four current values of 2·5, 3·0, 3·5 and 4·0 mA has been provided. The supply is from an 18 V dry battery, and the current selected is standardized by balancing the potential drop across a resistor against the standard voltage provided by a Weston cell. Provision is also made for backing off large bridge signals.

The mode of operation of the bridge is in effect one of constant current, because there is a large preponderance of ballast over bridge resistance in the 18 V circuit at all four current levels. This enhances the sensitivity of detection because of the negative temperature coefficient of resistance of the thermistors. The thermistor

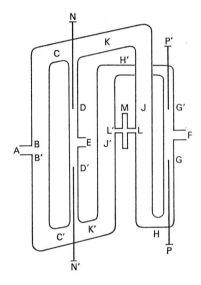

FIG. 30. Martin gas density balance (Martin and James, *Biochem. J.* **63**, 138 (1956)).

that is cooled by an increased flow of gas will increase in resistance and, taking a smaller proportion of the bridge current it will cool still further; the converse will be true for the other thermistor of the pair.

Martin gas-density balance. In this device, as in the Gow-Mac model, the density of the column effluent is compared with that of pure carrier gas. This version of the gas-density balance is shown in Fig. 30.

With carrier gas entering at both A and F, the flow compensating rods N, N', P and P' are adjusted so that there is no pressure difference between L and L', the two sides of the anemometer. In this state carrier gas entering at F will divide equally along G and G' so that the flow of gas at L and L' past the anemometer M are the same, the two flows eventually recombining at E. Carrier gas from the chromatographic column entering at A divides equally along B and B', also eventually combining at E. If a gas of greater density than that of the carrier gas enters the detector at *A*, the weight of this gas passing through *B'* will be greater than that through *B*. As a result of this, the pressure between *C* and *C'* will cause the flow of carrier gas from *F* to divide unequally along *G* and *G'*. In fact, in this example more will proceed via *G* and *L*, than along *G'* and *L'*, giving a flow of gas directly across the anemometer *M*.

As in the Gow-Mac model, only pure carrier gas passes over the sensing device, and the response is directly proportional to the density and hence molecular weight of the separated components of the sample mixture.

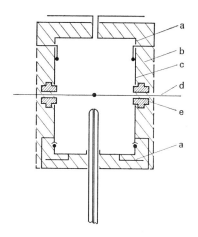

FIG. 31. Flame thermocouple detector (Scott, in *Vapour Phase Chromatography*, London, 1956). (a) Baffle plates, (b) asbestos wool, (c) metal housing, (d) thermocouple leads, (e) insulating supports.

Flame Detectors

Flame Thermocouple Detector

This detector, known also as the "heat of combustion" detector and shown diagrammatically in Fig. 31, was introduced by Scott [66, 67]. It has the advantage that both the detector and the associated electrical circuit required to operate it are fairly simple to construct. Hydrogen, either as carrier gas or as an additional gas supply introduced immediately after the chromatographic column, is burnt at a jet within the detector chamber. The top of the flame is arranged so as to terminate just below the hot junction of a thermocouple in the form of a small bead, about 1·5 mm in diameter, and made either of an iron–constantan alloy or of a platinum–iridium/palladium–gold alloy. The whole apparatus must be carefully shielded to eliminate draughts.

It is also necessary to ensure that the carrier gas supply system is leak proof, as the stability of the recorder base line depends very much upon accurate control of the flow of carrier gas. Vibration of the thermocouple bead must also be avoided if the detector is to work at a reasonable sensitivity. A supply of oxygen or air is required to ensure that all the organic components eluted from the chromatographic column are completely burnt in the flame. This flame can be ignited either manually or electrically, but in the former case, care must be taken not to incur mechanical damage to the thermocouple.

The detector is used as follows. The recorder sensitivity is adjusted to the required full-scale deflection using the potentiometer *R3* in Fig. 32. With the carrier gas flowing, the flame is ignited and the detector allowed to reach an equilibrium temperature. The recorder base line is then adjusted to a suitable position, using potentiometers *R1* and *R2*. The sample material is then injected on to the chromatographic column in the usual way. As the gaseous components are eluted from the column, the organic species present are burnt in the flame which lengthens and surrounds the thermocouple bead. The change in temperature of the bead is related to the molar heat of combustion of the compounds present. This change of temperature produces a current through the potentiometer *R3*, part of which is displayed on the recorder chart.

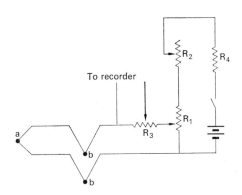

FIG. 32. Circuit of chromatograph based upon a flame thermocouple detector (Scott, in *Vapour Phase Chromatography*, London, 1956), *R1*, 50-ohm; *R2*, 250-ohm; *R3*, 50-ohm; *R4*, 500-ohm; a, hot junction; b, cold junctions.

The sensitivity of a flame thermocouple detector is comparable with that of a good thermal conductivity cell, although it is, of course, insensitive to the permanent gases. For some applications it is possible to use a flame thermocouple detector after the carrier gas with the separated sample components has passed through a thermal conductivity cell for this latter determination.

In its original form, this detector was used with hydrogen as carrier gas. This is not always convenient, and in a modification by Wirth [68], nitrogen gas is used as carrier, with the addition of hydrogen at a position between the end of the chromatographic column and the jet. The ratio of hydrogen to nitrogen (about 2:1) must be carefully controlled. Carbon monoxide has also been used as carrier gas with this detector [69], and has the advantage of producing a non-corrosive effluent gas, even when the sample components contain halogens.

Large concentrations of halogen-containing compounds may extinguish the flame. Sample components that do not burn, or burn only with difficulty, together also with carbon dioxide, water vapour and the permanent gases, give a small, sometimes negative response with this detector; its principal use is in the determination of the hydrocarbon gases, when these are present in major amounts.

Flame Emissivity Detector

In this detector the carrier gas from the column, usually nitrogen, is mixed in constant proportion with a combustible gas and burnt in a small chamber at a wide, stainless steel jet. In order to maintain combustion, a supply of air is blown into the base of the detector, where it diffuses through porcelain beads into the flame chamber. A metal reflector and condensing lens are used to focus light emitted from the flame on to a barrier layer photocell. The design of Grant [50, 51] is shown in Fig. 33.

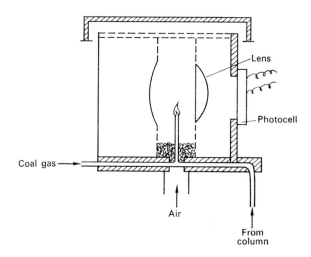

FIG. 33. Flame emissivity detector (Grant, *Proc. 2nd Symp. Gas Chromatog.*, Amsterdam, 1958).

The flame emission changes with change of carbon content of the carrier gas stream, and the detector therefore responds to organic compounds eluted from the chromatographic column. Although this detector will operate with a low background, the linearity of the response is increased by increasing the background emission. For this reason, coal gas was suggested as the combustible gas rather than pure hydrogen. Present day towns' gas will require the addition of small amounts of an organic compound, such as benzene, to give this background value.

The flame emissivity detector does not respond to the permanent gases. The response to n-paraffins appears to increase with increasing carbon number, but is small relative to the response given by aromatic hydrocarbons. There is thus a selectivity towards this *class* of organic compounds.

Although the flame emissivity detector as here described was proposed in 1958, it does not appear to have been extensively used. It was omitted from the first edition of this book as it has little application to gas analysis, and is included now only as the precursor of the more important flame photometric detector.

Flame Photometric Detector

The inclusion of a monochromator or of narrow-band optical filters converts the flame emissivity detector to the flame photometric detector. This technique of flame spectrum analysis, well developed for inorganic analysis, has been used by Crider [70] and by Brody and Chaney [71] as the basis for a new detector sensitive to parts per million amounts of sulphur compounds and even less of phosphorus compounds. It has found extensive use in the determination of minute amounts of phosphorus-containing pesticides in animal and vegetable residues. It is also of considerable importance in the field of atmospheric pollution monitoring of sulphur dioxide levels, and also where the analysis of gaseous mixture containing small quantities of sulphur compounds is required.

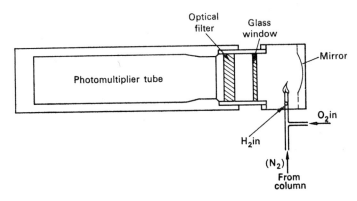

FIG. 34. Flame photometric detector (Brody and Chaney, *J. Gas Chromatog.* 43 (1966)).

The detector shown in Fig. 34 is usually employed with nitrogen as the carrier gas for the chromatographic separation; the effluent from the column is then mixed with air or oxygen to support the combustion of a hydrogen flame. Sulphur compounds present in the column effluent, burn to sulphur dioxide in the flame. Some formation of sulphur trioxide may also occur, but the amounts are small and do not appear to affect the functioning of the detector. Sulphur dioxide gives rise to a blue glow in the outer, cooler parts of the flame, with spectral emission in the region 300–425 nm. Measurement is made at 394 $\pm$ 5 nm, where the flame emission is almost specific for sulphur. The detector is sensitive to parts per billion amounts of sulphur and the response follows a square law, giving a straightline calibration on a log–log scale. The calibration curve for hydrogen sulphide, as would be expected, closely follows that for sulphur dioxide. Aliphatic thiols give a somewhat lower response. An increased sensitivity to sulphur was obtained by Crider and Slater [72] by establishing a background luminescence with sulphur dioxide and thus operating on a more sensitive portion of the response curve.

By including a collector electrode, the flame photometric detector housing can incorporate also a flame ionization detector. The composite detector operates in the normal modes of the two individual detectors, giving two outputs responding respectively to sulphur compounds (FPD) and to organic (FD). This composite form has found application in the field of atmospheric pollution monitoring [73].

Other Flame Detectors

Two further examples of detectors using flame techniques, the flame ionization detector (FID) and the alkali flame ionization detector (AID) are described in the following chapter devoted to ionization detectors.

Electrochemical Detectors

The Hersch Cell

A simple form of the Hersch cell can be used as a sensitive and specific detector for oxygen. In this form [74, 75] it consists of a caustic electrolyte contained by a porous diaphragm with a cathode in the form of a silver metal coil or gauze. A lead rod is used as a node. Oxygen is reduced at the cathode with the generation of an electric current:

$$(O) + H_2O + 2e^- = 2OH^-$$
$$Pb + 3OH^- + 2e^- = PbO(OH)^- + H_2O$$

Advantages claimed for this detector include linearity of response to oxygen up to 1%, the ability to analyse a number of streams sequentially with the one detector and the somewhat simplified chromatographic separation necessary. For example, molecular sieves can then be used at room temperature for determining oxygen in the presence of argon.

Coulometric Detectors

These detectors consist of two separate units, a pyrolysis furnace followed by a titration unit. In its original form, as introduced by Liberti and Cartoni [76], the carbon content of the material under examination was converted to carbon dioxide

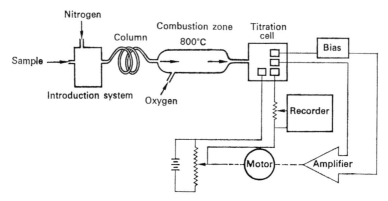

Fig. 35. Microcoulometric detector (Coulson, *Amer. Lab.* p. 23, (1969)).

in the pyrolysis unit placed immediately after the chromatographic column. The carbon dioxide in the carrier gas stream was titrated coulometrically, giving a coulometer current as the detector response. Selective detectors have been described by Coulson and Cavanagh [77] for compounds containing chlorine and by Adams *et al.* [78] for compounds containing sulphur.

A block diagram of a gas chromatograph fitted with a microcoulometric detector is shown in Fig. 35. This particular example [79] is used for the determination of chlorine in organic materials. Hydrogen chloride (together with hydrogen bromide and iodide if organic compounds containing bromine and iodine are present) is produced in the pyrolysis unit, and the chloride, bromide or iodide ions are titrated with electrically generated silver ions. In the sulphur detector, sulphur and sulphur compounds are converted to sulphur dioxide in the pyrolysis unit, and are then titrated iodometrically with electrically generated iodine.

These detectors are not very sensitive, but have the advantage that the chlorine, sulphur, etc., content can be calculated directly from a knowledge of Faraday's Law; the amount of material titrated, W g, is given by

$$W = \frac{It \times \text{eq. wt.} \times 10^6}{96,500}$$

where $I = $ titrant generator current (amps),
$t = $ time (seconds).

A coulometric detector for the selective determination of nitrogen compounds has been described by Martin [80].

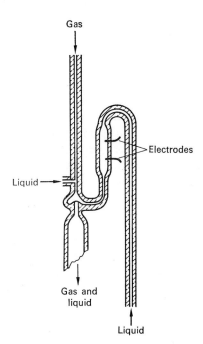

FIG. 36. Electrolytic conductivity detector cell (Coulson, *Amer. Lab.*, p. 27 (1969)).

Electrolytic Conductivity Detector

This detector, shown diagramatically in Fig. 36, was developed by Coulson [81] to meet the need for increased sensitivity. The liquid, usually but not necessarily deionized water, absorbs the sulphur dioxide, hydrogen chloride or ammonia to give a weak electrolyte. The conductivity of this electrolyte is measured between platinum electrodes and recorded using a potentiometric recorder in the usual way. In addition to being more sensitive than the microcoulometric detector, it has the advantages of being less expensive and easier to operate. The selectivity is retained, the detector being sensitive to the halogens, sulphur and nitrogen, and insensitive to carbon, hydrogen and oxygen in organic compounds.

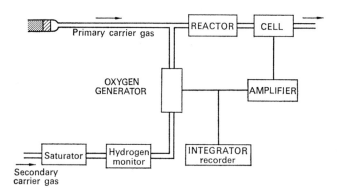

FIG. 37. Reaction coulometer (Burton *et al.*, *6th Symp. Gas Chromatog.*, Rome, 1966, paper 14).

Reaction Coulometer

In this detector, introduced by Burton *et al.* [82], the gas eluted from the chromatographic column is mixed with a second stream of gas containing electrolytically generated oxygen, and then passed to a reactor where the organic vapour present is burned. The gases then pass to a cell sensitive to oxygen concentration. The electrical output of this cell is transmitted to the electrolytic oxygen generator via a negative feed-back circuit and amplifier. The generator then increases the oxygen supply to make good the deficiency of the gas stream. Thus the oxygen produced by the generator is a measure of the amount of organic compound being burnt. This form of the detector shown in Fig. 37 is known also as a "combustion coulometer".

An alternative form, known also as a "hydrogenation coulometer", based upon the same principle, uses hydrogen in place of oxygen [83]. It is sensitive only to reducible components such as unsaturated carbon compounds.

CHAPTER 5

Detectors (continued)

Ionization Detectors

These detectors are all based upon the conduction of electricity by gases. Under normal conditions gases do not conduct electricity, but if an energy source is used to promote ionization of the gas then, under the influence of an electric field, the gas will become conducting. The energy sources commonly used to promote ionization are hydrogen flames or radioactive isotopes such as strontium-90.

This type of detector is more sensitive than most katharometers and the gas-density balance and can therefore be used to detect the components of very small samples. The need for detectors with this increased sensitivity was a direct outcome of the development of capillary columns forecast by Martin [38] at an International Symposium in 1956. This combination of sensitive detector and capillary column has led to greatly increased chromatographic efficiency for many types of separation. These ionization detectors are, in general, more selective than most of the detectors previously described, and some of these particular applications can be extended to the field of gas analysis. The first of these detectors to be described was the ionization cross-section detector [49], known also as the β-ray ionization detector, which was based upon a suggestion of Pompeo and Otvos [84], and introduced at the 1956 Symposium.

It has been noted by Lovelock [85] that when the ion density in an ionization chamber is low, the current flowing across the chamber under the influence of an applied electric field will increase with increase of field strength until a constant value of the current is obtained corresponding to the collection of all the ions generated within the chamber. This value of the current is known as the saturation or standing current of the cell. The field strength necessary to reach this saturation current will depend upon the nature of the gas in the chamber and upon the extent of ionization of the gas, i.e. the ionization density. At much higher field strengths, a further increase of current occurs; this is attributed to a number of causes, the most important being the ionization of the gas by the applied field. The range of applied potential over which the saturation current flows decreases with increase of ionization density.

During the course of an analysis, the applied field is maintained at sufficient strength to ensure saturation current. Under these conditions, when a component of the sample under examination passes from the chromatographic column to the ionization chamber, it provides an increase in ion density and therefore a change of current flowing across the cell.

At atmospheric pressure and with the low ion densities used, loss of ions from the gas in the chamber can occur either by collection, giving rise to the standing current across the cell, or by recombination. This recombination effect is less likely to be recorded in argon or nitrogen used as carrier gas, than in air. Another effect encountered in some ionization detectors is the formation of a charged "space cloud" around the cathode, leading to extensive recombination even in argon, if the collection of ions is impeded. This effect can be particularly serious at high ion densities. Both recombination and space charge effects can be reduced considerably by using a small chamber volume and a high field strength. This field strength is limited by the tendency of excess applied potential to cause ionization of the gas on its own account.

Ionization detectors have the advantage that precise temperature control is not required and that the carrier gas flow rate is not as critical as when a katharometer or gas-density balance is used. Ionization detectors are, however, very sensitive to contaminants occasionally present in the carrier gas. For this reason it is recommended that the carrier gas should be purified by passage through a trap in the supply line. This trap should be packed with pellets of molecular sieve and, where extreme sensitivity is required, can also be immersed in liquid nitrogen. This additional refinement is not necessary for most of the applications to gas analysis, but the inclusion of a trap operating at room temperature is well worth while.

A further disadvantage of ionization detectors is that even the simplest requires a relatively expensive amplification stage. For this reason most ionization detectors are used in association with commercial gas chromatographs, in contrast to the extensive use of thermal conductivity cells with home made apparatus.

Cross-section Ionization Detector

This, the first of the ionization detectors to be described, has not been as widely employed as those that have been developed from it, such as the argon ionization detector. Although the argon cell is very much more sensitive, the cross-section detector is more versatile. It can, for example, be used with any carrier gas, will detect all gases, has a linear response over a wide concentration range and this response can be calculated from known ionization cross-section parameters (when using helium or more frequently argon, ionization effects can cause trouble). The molecular ionization cross-section of any compound is the sum of the atomic cross-sections of its components, and it is therefore possible to predict the relative chromatographic response of a given substance. The peak area should be divided by a factor

$$\frac{Q_c - Q_a}{M_c}$$

to give a value R;

where Q_c = relative cross-section for the component,

Q_a = relative cross-section for the carrier gas, and

M_c = molecular weight of the component.

R divided by Σ*R* then gives the wt. % of the particular component. Some relative atomic cross-sections are given in Table 7, together with some examples of derived molecular cross-sections.

TABLE 7. SOME RELATIVE IONIZATION CROSS-SECTIONS (H = 1) [86]

Gas	Relative cross-section
Helium	0·694
Nitrogen	3·84 (N_2 = 7·68)
Oxygen	3·29 (O_2 = 6·58)
Fluorine	1·85
Neon	1·75
Chlorine	11·8 (Cl_2 = 23·6)
Bromine	18·0
Argon	10·9
Krypton	17·4
Xenon	24·1
Carbon monoxide	7·45
Carbon dioxide	10·74
Methane	8·17
Ethylene	12·32
Ethane	14·32

It is difficult to understand why a detector with such obvious advantages has not been more widely used, although this may be largely due to the simplicity and relative cheapness of chromatographs based upon thermal conductivity cells. Both the katharometer and ionization cross-section detectors require sample aliquots of the order of 1 ml in order to detect the components of such mixtures as water gas or towns' gas, and neither detector responds adequately to components present to an extent of less than about 100 ppm.

A diagrammatic form of this detector is shown in Fig. 38. The source of ionizing radiation produces a steady concentration of ion pairs in the carrier gas as it passes through the detector chamber. The β-active isotope strontium-90 is usually employed for this, with an average radiation range greater than the ionization path within the radiation chamber. With a heavy carrier gas, increased ionization occurs within the chamber and conversely, less ionization occurs when hydrogen or helium are used. The greatest sensitivity is obtained at low values of the saturation current, obtained with either hydrogen or helium as carrier gas.

The collecting anode should be of a reasonable size, with a diameter of at least one-third that of the cell, and should be maintained at a potential in the range 500–1000 V. Under these conditions recombination effects and space-charge formations do not occur, and the response produced by the detector is independent of small changes of potential, gas flow rate or temperature.

The thick walls of the chamber absorb all excess β-radiation and, although care should be taken in handling the detector, accidental exposure to harmful radiation is unlikely to occur. Under normal conditions it should not be necessary to take the detector to pieces, and if a fault develops in the detector itself, it should be returned to the makers.

A micro-ionization cross-section detector has been described by Lovelock *et al.* [87], in which the chamber volume can be reduced to less than 0·1 ml. For the ionizing source, the long life, safety and convenience of tritium outweigh the disadvantage of possible loss of tritium under extreme operating conditions. This detector is very much more sensitive than the macro model to the amount of gaseous component passing through it, but neither detector is sensitive to low component concentrations.

In the field of gas analysis, the chief use of the cross-section ionization detector is in the determination of the permanent gases when present in major amounts.

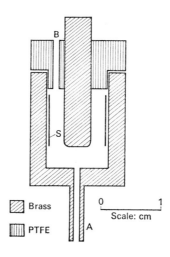

Fig. 38. Cross-section ionization detector (Lovelock, *Analyt. Chem.* **33**, 167 (1961)). A, chromatographic column; B, gas outlet; C, source.

Argon Ionization Detector

The argon ionization detector, or argon cell as it is frequently called, was first described by Lovelock [40, 88, 89]. Although very sensitive to organic materials in general, it is insensitive to the lower hydrocarbon gases and also to the permanent gases. It does, however, have a few particular applications in gas analysis, and is included here for that reason.

Under normal operating conditions, the argon carrier gas is subjected to ionization radiation from a suitable source. Radium-D, radon-226, strontium-90, promethium-147 and tritium have all been used for this purpose. In this irradiation positive ions and free electrons are produced. These electrons, collected under the influence of the applied field, give rise to a small current—the standing current across the cell. In addition, a proportion of the argon molecules are excited by the radiation to produce metastable but un-ionized atoms. These excited atoms decay rapidly, and in returning to the ground state emit ultra-violet radiation.

Under the influence of the high field strengths that are used with this detector, the production of metastable argon atoms is greatly enhanced, and exceeds that of the simple ion formation that is the basis of the cross-section ionization detector.

The energy stored in the excited argon atoms is sufficient to cause ionization of the molecules of the introduced sample components as they enter the ionization chamber. These additional ions are collected by the anode, giving rise to the current increase through the cell that constitutes the detector response. When operated in this way, the argon ionization detector has a high signal to background ratio, and the response is additive, that is in the same direction as the standing current through the cell.

TABLE 8. IONIZATION POTENTIALS OF SOME GASES
[90]

Gas	Ionization potential, eV
Acetylene	11·6
Ammonia	11·2
Carbon monoxide	14·1
Carbon dioxide	14·4
Chlorine	13·2
Ethane	12·8
Ethylene	12·2
Hydrogen	15·6
Hydrogen chloride	13·8
Hydrogen sulphide	10·4
Methane	14·5
Oxygen	14·1
Nitrogen	15·5
Nitric oxide	9·5
Nitrous oxide	12·9
Nitrogen dioxide	11·0
Sulphur dioxide	13·1

The excitation potential of metastable argon is 11·7 eV, and only molecules with a lower ionization potential than this will be ionized in the chamber. As shown in Table 8, a few of the common gases are in this category, but only the determination of nitric oxide, nitrogen dioxide and hydrogen sulphide is likely to be of any importance.

In order to prevent excessive current flowing across the ionization chamber when the sample components are admitted, the cell is designed so that the space-charge effect is always present, this serves to limit the current. Lovelock has stated that the primary electron beam across the detector is confined to a narrow channel between the source and the anode. The sensing volume is therefore appreciably smaller than the geometric volume. From a consideration of this, Lovelock [91] has developed the argon ionization triode detector, in which a third electrode is introduced into the ionization chamber in a form coaxial with the anode. This electrode does not interfere with the collection of electrons or of negative ions by the anode, but does collect the positive ions that normally give rise to the background current. The argon ionization triode has therefore a very much reduced noise level, the noise being related to the background current. In addition, the triode is reported to be more sensitive than the argon ionization detector.

The residual positive ion background current of the triode can be reduced still further by introducing a fourth electrode, carrying a positive charge, between the collector electrode (i.e. the third electrode), and the anode.

A more frequently used variation of the argon ionization detector is the micro-argon cell. In this, the anode is positioned in a small recess or cavity at one end of the cell, and the electric field distribution has been modified to give a much smaller effective volume to the cell. This design has been developed for use with capillary columns, and is shown in Fig. 39, together with the argon cell and the argon triode detector.

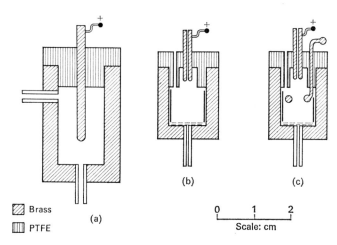

FIG. 39. Argon ionization detectors (Lovelock, *Proc. 3rd Symp. Gas Chromatog.*, Edinburgh, 1960). (a) argon cell, (b) micro argon cell, (c) argon triode.

Attempts have been made, for example by Galwey [92], to use the argon cell for the determination of the permanent gases, but in these applications the mode of action of the argon cell is clearly not that of an argon ionization detector, nor that of a cross-section ionization detector, previously considered.

An annular design of detector that makes more efficient use of this anomalous response of an argon cell to the permanent gases has been described by Shahin and Lipsky [93]. This design, shown in Fig. 40, requires a field strength of only 1–2 V, tritium as the ionizing source, and has a very low internal volume.

When used with hydrogen or nitrogen as carrier gas, and with a somewhat higher field strength, this detector has a response that is strictly a function of the difference between the ionization cross-section of the sample, and that of the carrier. When argon is used as carrier gas, with an applied field of no more than 2 V, an increased ionization is obtained from the detector with samples of the permanent gases. This phenomenon appears to be characteristic of ionization chambers that feature small electrode separation of either coaxial or parallel plate geometry.

As with the cross-section ionization detector, the argon cell is relatively insensitive to changes of gas flow rate or of temperature. The response of the argon cell is closely related to the mass of the separated components. This has been demonstrated experimentally by Rouayheb *et al.* [94] for a wide range of hydrocarbon compounds using a micro-argon cell and a capillary column.

The argon ionization detector cannot be used for the determination of compounds that possess strong electron capture properties, such as are exhibited by compounds containing halogen atoms. Other limitations are imposed by the loss of

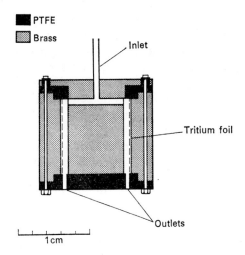

FIG. 40. Annular design of argon cell (Shahin and Lipsky, *Analyt. Chem.* **35,** 468 (1963)).

sensitivity that occurs when large quantities of water or air are introduced into the detector chamber.

The determination of trace amounts of the permanent gases. The conventional form of the argon ionization detector cannot be used for the determination of trace amounts of the permanent gases, or of many other gaseous compounds. However, a number of methods have been developed for determining small amounts of gases at low concentrations, using what is essentially either a cross-section or an argon ionization detector but using it in an unconventional way. Three such methods have been described, all of which are of general application to permanent gas analysis. They are usually referred to as:

(i) the helium ionization detector,
(ii) the "contaminated argon" method, and
(iii) the electron mobility detector.

Each of these developments will be considered in turn.

(i) *The helium ionization detector.* Argon is not the only gas that can be excited by a source of ionizing radiation to give atoms in a metastable state, this behaviour being shared by all the gases in the inert or noble gas group. The excitation potentials of this metastable state are too low to be of any use in the case of krypton or of xenon, whilst those of the remaining gases, helium and neon, are so high that metastable atoms are formed only with difficulty. This is because impurities present in these gases are converted to ions by collision with metastable atoms at a faster rate than metastable atoms are themselves formed. In order to obtain a reasonable population of metastable atoms in helium or neon used as carrier gas, a very pure supply is required. In practice only helium, with an excitation potential of 19·8 eV is used.

When the normal (i.e. impure) supply of helium is used, the introduction of a permanent gas into the chamber produces a decrease of ions and hence a decrease of the current flowing across the detector. It has been noted by Wiseman [95] that as the purity of the helium is increased, the standing current increases, and that at a certain point in the purity, the current response for an introduced sample is no longer subtractive but additive. Helium gas of purity greater than this is required for the operation of the helium ionization detector. Elaborate precautions may be necessary to ensure the removal of impurities if a supply of the required purity is not available.

In practice this means employing a purification train consisting of a titanium furnace at a temperature of 800–1000° to remove oxygen and nitrogen, hopcalite at 300° to remove hydrogen and molecular sieve at room temperature to remove water vapour. Using this technique, helium gas with a purity of greater than 99·999 % can be obtained, which gives positive peaks for all permanent gases.

It is usually necessary to modify the existing argon ionization cells for use with helium, as it is essential to keep all traces of air and water vapour from diffusing back into the ionization chamber. Even very small quantities introduced in this way have the same effect as reducing the purity of the helium supply.

This detector, developed by Berry [96, 18], responds to all the permanent gases except of course, helium itself, and can detect as little as 50 ppm by volume of these gases in a total volume as little as 10 μl.

(ii) *The "contaminated argon" method.* This method of using an argon ionization detector was described by Willis [97] and by Ellis and Forrest [98]. A "contaminant" such as ethylene is introduced into the argon carrier gas supply to an extent of a few parts per hundred million. When these hydrocarbon molecules undergo collision with the metastable argon atoms in the ionization chamber, ions are produced which, on collection at the anode in the usual way give rise to a current flow across the cell. This condition represents the steady-state operation of the detector.

When permanent gas molecules are introduced into the ionization chamber, the mean electron velocity is lowered by collision, and hence the proportion of argon atoms that are excited by the ionizing radiation decreases. This in turn reduces the amount of ethylene that can be ionized and hence results in a decrease of current across the cell, this decrease being the detector response to the introduced sample components.

The same result is obtained when helium is used as carrier gas, diluted in the same way with a few parts per hundred million of a suitable contaminant. There is little change of sensitivity when argon is replaced by helium as the contaminated carrier gas, both methods being greatly inferior in sensitivity to the method using the helium ionization detector.

(iii) *Electron mobility detector*. In the normal type of argon cell, the source of ionizing radiation is usually a fairly active β-emitter such as strontium-90. This can be replaced by a weak β-emitter such as tritium. The activity of the tritium is so weak, and the cell dimensions so arranged, that in the absence of an electric field the electrons from the source will not reach the anode.

The high potential applied to the anode of the conventional argon detector is now replaced by short pulses of 50–100 V. The duration of each pulse is arranged so that when only pure argon carrier gas is flowing, the number of electrons reaching the anode is very small, and the standing current is therefore also very small. When the permanent gas components of the sample are introduced into the chamber, the mean agitation velocity of the electrons is reduced, thus enabling them to be collected by the anode, giving rise to a current that constitutes the detector signal. When this detector, described by Lovelock [99], is operated at a frequency of 0·27 Mc/s it responds to all except the noble gases.

The response of the detector is linear with gas concentrations of up to 1% by volume of such diatomic gases as hydrogen, oxygen and nitrogen. Although argon is the preferred carrier gas, it can be replaced by helium or by nitrogen, with some loss of sensitivity.

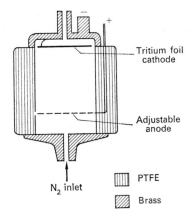

Tritium foil
cathode

Adjustable
anode

N₂ inlet

PTFE

Brass

Fᴵɢ. 41. Parallel plate electron capture ionization detector (Shandon Scientific Co. Ltd.).

Electron Capture Ionization Detector (Fig. 41)

This detector described by Lovelock and Lipsky [100], is known also as the electron absorption detector. It has been noted that the ion recombination effects that can occur with the use of the argon ionization detector, are particularly troublesome when the mixtures for analysis contain compounds with halogen atoms. This effect has been used to advantage in the design of the electron capture detector, which is therefore particularly sensitive to halogen and other compounds with high electron affinities.

The components of the gaseous mixtures form negative ions in the ionization chamber by the process of electron capture. These negative ions combine with the positive ions present at a faster rate than do the free electrons, thus giving rise to a marked decrease in the standing current across the cell.

Radium-D and strontium-90 have been used as sources for electron capture detectors, but the best choice appears to be tritium or nickel-63. The short range of the ionizing radiation ensures that most of the energy is dissipated within the detector, no additional shielding is necessary, and the radiation hazard is neglible in comparison with that of radium-D or strontium-90.

Argon has been used as carrier gas, but is not recommended[101] owing to the excitation process whereby metastable argon atoms are formed. Helium has also been used, but is also not recommended owing to the decrease in ion recombination that occurs following the large number of elastic collisions between helium atoms and the positive and negative ions. The preferred carrier gas is nitrogen which is free from these two effects. For maximum sensitivity, the nitrogen supply should be free from impurities, particularly water vapour.

It is possible to obtain quite large erroneous and anomalous signals from an electron capture detector. A consideration of these has led Lovelock to suggest the use of a pulsed electron capture detector [102], which whilst retaining the simplicity and sensitivity of the d.c. electron capture detector is free from these erroneous and anomalous responses.

The electron capture detector, unlike the other ionization detectors, functions by a process that is essentially one of electron absorption. The current across the cell is a function of the number N of electrons reaching the anode per second. In the presence of a concentration c of the absorbing species, then

$$N = N_0 . e^{-kcx}$$

where N_0 is the standing current across the cell in the absence of the absorbing species, k is the electron capture cross-section of this species, and x is a proportionality constant [102]. This equation, resembling that derived from the Beer–Lambert law, can also be deduced from a consideration of the electron capture mechanism as light absorption at the wavelength range 0·7–7 nm.

Particular uses of this detector include the detection and determination of the free halogens and the halogenated hydrocarbons. The free halogens are all very corrosive, and special care is required to ensure that damage to the cell or more particularly to the radioactive source, does not occur. If such gases are to be examined, the detector should be constructed of an inert material such as PTFE, with a resistant metal (e.g. nickel) anode.

Photo-ionization Detector

In this detector [103], the separated components of the sample carried in the stream of inert carrier gas, are ionized by photons of appropriate energy. Helium may be used as carrier gas at atmospheric pressure, but for other carrier gases it is necessary to use reduced pressures of less than 100 mm, such as can be obtained using an ordinary laboratory water pump.

The photo-ionization detector does not respond to the permanent gases, but is particularly suited for the determination of ionizable gases present as contaminants in air or in any other non-ionizable gas.

Flame Ionization Detector

The flame ionization detector [41, 104] is the simplest of all the ionization detectors, yet has a sensitivity comparable with that of the argon cell. The organic

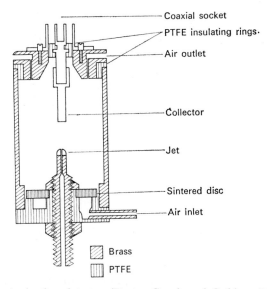

FIG. 42. Flame ionization detector (Desty, Geach and Goldup, *Proc. 3rd Symp. Gas Chromatog.*, Edinburgh, 1960).

components of the sample under investigation provide the source of ions by burning in a jet of hydrogen. Any carrier gas can be used with this detector. When carrier gases other than H_2 are used, hydrogen gas is admitted to the carrier stream after the chromatographic column, but before reaching the detector, in order to provide the flame in which the organic compounds are burnt. A hydrogen flow rate of the order of 50 ml per minute is generally used.

A form of the detector is shown in Fig. 42 [105]. The jet is generally used as the cathode. The ions formed during the combustion are collected by the anode (often a small piece of metal gauze), maintained at a suitable potential above that of the cathode—usually in the range 100–300 V. This is considerably less than the potential required for the operation of the argon ionization detector.

As with the flame thermocouple detector, the hydrogen flame can be ignited either manually or electrically, and should be allowed to reach an equilibrium temperature before adjustments are made to the amplifier. The distance between the anode and the cathode is important but not critical. The current output of the flame ionization detector is said to bear a linear relation to the molar construction of the organic material, and also to be proportional to the carbon number in a homologous series.

The flame ionization detector does not respond to the permanent gases, and is insensitive to water vapour. It is therefore a very suitable detector for the determination of trace amounts of hydrocarbon gases in air or in other inorganic gaseous mixtures. A flame ionization detector has also been used for the determination of the halogen gases [106].

A certain amount of the background noise associated with this detector can be eliminated by using a reference jet of burning hydrogen. This system has been reported by McWilliam [107] as giving still greater sensitivity than the simple single jet detector.

Just as the argon ionization detector has been modified to give a triode detector, so a third electrode can be inserted into the ionization chamber of the flame ionization detector, enabling it to be used as an a.c. amplifier. Middlehurst and Kennett [108] reported that the detector signal from an a.c. modulated triode is large enough to be recorded without additional amplification. The introduction of further electrodes was also considered as a possible means of improving the characteristics of the triode detector.

Alkali Flame Ionization Detector

It has been observed that the ionization of a hydrogen flame can be considerably enhanced by the presence of sodium, when certain inorganic elements such as phosphorus or chlorine are introduced into the flame [109]. This observation forms the basis of a flame ionization detector with greatly increased sensitivity towards phosphorus and certain of the halogen elements. The mechanism appears to be that the products of combustion of compounds containing these elements react with the alkali metal probe to increase the rate of release of sodium from it. The sodium vapour is then excited and ionized in the flame [110].

In the earlier designs of detector, the alkali metal was supported on a stainless steel mesh. Such screens tend to lose their ability to give this increased flame ionization, partly because of disintegration of the alkali layer and partly because of changing molecular species of alkali metal on the screen [111]. This loss of sensitivity complicates the use of the detector in this form. In latter forms, the hydrogen gas passes through a pressed salt tip, and the flame burns on the salt surface.

The base current of an alkali flame ionization detector is about one hundred times greater than that of a conventional flame ionization detector, but the noise level is increased as well. The ionization current increases with the presence of phosphorus and halogens, giving a greatly enhanced sensitivity for these elements. The detector responds also to sulphur compounds but as shown by Dressler and Janak [112] the maximum response appears to be in the form of a decrease of ionization current, although this signal can change direction with change of base current across the flame.

The alkali metal salts suggested by the earlier workers were the sulphates and chlorides of sodium and potassium, although lithium, rubidium and caesium chlorides have also been proposed. Karmen [110] reported that this detector was sensitive to compounds containing chlorine, bromine and iodine, but not fluorine. The relative flame response of the three halogens depended upon the choice of alkali metal screen.

Radioactivity Detectors

Both Geiger tubes and scintillation counters have been used to detect and determine radioactive components present in the chromatographic column effluent. These detectors can often be combined with some other form of non-destructive detector, such as a thermal conductivity cell as described by Kokes *et al.* [113]. Radioactivity detectors are not used extensively in the field of gas analysis, but are of value for particular applications.

An unusual form of radioactivity detector is that described by Gudzinowicz and Smith [114], in which the source of radioactivity is a krypton-95 quinol clathrate, which on exposure to inorganic oxidants, releases radioactive krypton atoms which are subsequently detected using a Geiger tube. This detector has been used to determine 1–20 ppm of fluorine in air. Bromine, nitrogen dioxide, chlorine, OF_2, NO_2F and NO_2Cl also have a high reactivity with the krypton-85 clathrate.

CHAPTER 6

Apparatus for Gas Analysis

IN order to make quantitative determinations by gas chromatography it is necessary to inject known quantities of the material being examined on to the correct column, and to pass the separated components in turn to a suitable detector. These three parts, the injector, column and detector which form the essential parts of all gas chromatographs, have been considered in turn. In order to complete the apparatus required to undertake analyses by gas chromatography, it is necessary also to be able to introduce, measure, and regulate the supply of the correct carrier gas, to maintain the selected column and detector at a predetermined temperature and to record and interpret the response obtained from the detector. These aspects are considered in this present chapter.

Carrier Gas Supply

The most frequently used carrier gases are argon, nitrogen and helium, although for particular applications other gases have been used. For example, the Janak [54] method of gas analysis using a gas absorption burette as the integral detector required the use of carbon dioxide as carrier gas, a hydrogen–nitrogen mixture has been used with a flame ionization detector, and for the determination of argon a method has been described using oxygen as the carrier gas [115].

Whatever gas is used, it is generally available in the form of a cylinder supply at a pressure of up to 2500 lb/in². In almost all chromatographic applications it is necessary to use a two-stage regulator to reduce the pressure of this cylinder supply to a working pressure of a few pounds above atmospheric. In addition to this control, it is often advisable to incorporate a needle valve into the gas flow system to ensure a stable flow through the apparatus.

An alternative means of limiting carrier gas flow through parts of an apparatus is to use capillary tubing as part of the gas line. This device has been used successfully to control the flow of carrier gas through the two gas supply lines required to operate a gas-density balance detector.

The simplest way of measuring the flow of carrier gas is to insert a flow meter such as a Rotameter in the supply line. These meters are calibrated for particular gases, and density corrections are necessary if they are used with other carrier gases. They are liable to result in small pressure fluctuations which can be picked up electrically on the recording device and so affect the output noise level.

Another flow measuring device, usually known as a soap film meter, is shown in Fig. 43. It consists of a suitably calibrated burette through which the carrier gas passes and a reservoir containing soap solution [116]. The rate of travel of gas through the burette is observed with the aid of a soap film formed across the tube, together with a stop watch. Where this method of timing is not sufficiently precise, the soap film may be made conductive by the addition of sodium carbonate and electrical timing employed [117].

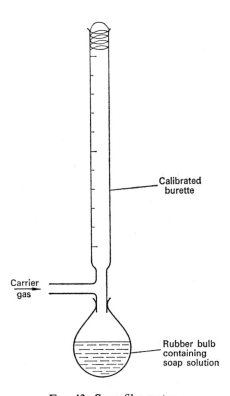

FIG. 43. Soap film meter.

The pressure drop across a film is very small, and for all practical purposes, may be neglected. Pure soap solution is now seldom employed, although the name 'soap film meter' is still commonly used. Any one of a wide range of surfactants can be employed—a (1 + 4) dilution of Teepol in water being commonly recommended.

Although used largely in the intermediate ranges, no real difficulty exists in constructing and using soap film meters to measure from about 1 ml per hour up to about 500 l. per hour. These meters are usually placed at the end of the carrier gas flow line, prior to the vent to atmosphere. This is necessary to avoid deterioration of the chromatographic column and interference by water with the functioning of the detector.

The response given by certain detectors is particularly sensitive to change of carrier gas flow rate. Examples that have been given are the flame thermocouple detector and certain designs of thermal conductivity cell. Most work has been done using a thermal conductivity cell, and an example of the relation between the response of this detector and the carrier gas flow rate is shown in Fig. 44. The peak area response increases with decrease of carrier gas flow rate. Optimum values of peak height response are generally observed or indicated at low flow rates. The example illustrated refers to hydrogen sulphide in air [118], but is typical of many other cases.

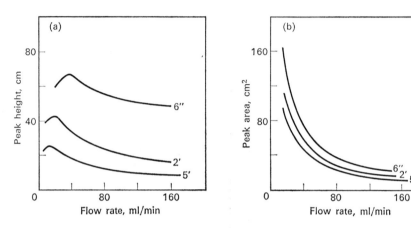

FIG. 44. Variation of detector response with change of carrier gas flow rate. (a) peak height measurement, (b) peak area measurement. Column: 6 in. silica gel; detector: thermal conductivity cell; carrier gas: hydrogen; bridge current 300 mA; sample gas: 40% air, 60% hydrogen sulphide.

Temperature Control

The accurate control of temperature is of greater importance in gas analysis than in many other applications of gas chromatography, as so many of the separations are made at or near room temperature. Whilst it is fairly easy to construct a thermostat that will maintain an enclosed space at a temperature of 80° or more, it is a much greater problem to maintain a temperature of, say, 30° accurately for long periods.

One design of thermostat enclosure now used at the authors' laboratory to accommodate a gas chromatograph based upon a katharometer is in the form of a double box. The outer case is lined on the inside with an insulating layer of expanded polystyrene 1 in. thick. The remaining space, about 3 in. wide, around the inner cabinet is filled with air circulating at a controlled temperature. This circulation is maintained by a small blower motor, fitted externally to the rear panel. Suitably placed baffles are used to ensure good hot-air distribution over the whole surface of the inner compartment. Heat is provided by four 240 V, 125 W covered, flat-strip elements mounted in the air passages below the inner box, and connected in a series–parallel arrangement to give a total capacity of about 125 W, with a high surface area-heat dissipation ratio. An adjustable probe-type thermostat is used in conjunction with a hot wire vacuum switch. In addition, a small bimetallic switch requiring manual resetting is also incorporated in the heating circuit and set to a temperature of 35°.

Improvements subsequently made to this design have been the inclusion of a double front to the box and the positioning of the heaters, this time as bare wires, in the space between the inner and outer walls of the double box. Normal methods of observing temperature changes have not indicated any temperature fluctuations within the inner case.

In contrast to the more widely known applications of gas–liquid chromatography, elevated temperatures are seldom necessary for gas analysis. When these are required, the conventional vapour jacket, oil-filled bath or hot-air oven can be employed. Liquids that have been used in vapour jackets in the course of gas analysis include acetone b.p. 56·2°, methanol b.p. 64·7°, carbon tetrachloride b.p. 76·8 (attack of aluminium columns has been noted using this material in a vapour jacket), ethanol b.p. 78·4°, benzene b.p. 80·1°, water b.p. 100° and toluene b.p. 110·6°. Carbon tetrachloride and benzene are not recommended.

For certain applications it is advantageous to use temperatures below those of normal air temperatures. Thus, for example, the separation of oxygen from argon on a column packed with molecular sieve is accomplished [119] by maintaining the column at a temperature of −72°, neon can be separated from helium at −78° [120] and hydrogen deuteride–deuterium mixtures can be resolved at the temperature of liquid nitrogen −196° [121].

A convenient way of obtaining temperatures below those of normal working is to use a vapour jacket containing a volatile halogenated material such as dichlorodifluoromethane (freon 12), in conjunction with a condensing system adapted for use with a coolant such as solid carbon dioxide or liquid nitrogen.

Chromatographic Response

The response given by an integral detector is of the kind shown in Fig. 1 (p. 6). The height of the step is a measure of the detector function, and hence of the quantity of the component giving the peak. The corresponding response from a differential detector is also given in Fig. 1. The displacement of the curve from the base line in this case records the concentration of the component in the detector at that particular time. This differential response can be integrated automatically by a separate instrument or by a recorder designed to do this, or more simply by measuring the area contained between the chromatographic peak and the peak base.

This area measurement is easily made using a planimeter, but such a procedure is time consuming, and not suited to routine analysis. Calculation of peak areas from measurements of the peak height and peak width at half peak height is no improvement, particularly when the peaks are asymmetric.

The most satisfactory way of measuring the area of a chromatographic peak is by means of a device known as an integrator, which provides a record of the integrated chromatographic response. This may be achieved mechanically, electrically or electronically, and a number of models are commercially available. Probably the greatest disadvantage of this method of measurement is that it is usually necessary to possess some idea of what the magnitude of the response is likely to be *before* the component starts to elute, as any change in sensitivity (range switching) during elution will invalidate the integration. This disadvantage is not encountered with measurements based upon peak heights, and can be minimised though not entirely eliminated by using a wide range integrator. For best results, provision should be made for automatic base line correction (base line drift) and for recorder instability. Such instruments are expensive.

Integrator output can be in a number of forms, of which the most satisfying is a print out giving both integrated areas and retention times. Less sophisticated integrators may use a 2-pen recorder, of which one pen traces step functions or marker lines at the edge of the differential record.

In place of the integrator, peak areas can be obtained via a continuous record of the detector response, as for example on magnetic or paper tape, which is processed by a simple computer.

It should perhaps be pointed out that the ability of the integrator to measure true peak areas will depend very largely upon the base-line stability. If there is no deviation of the base line when only carrier gas is flowing, then the minutest signal can be used to initiate the integration and a true area will be recorded. However, if deviations ("noise" or "grass") are superimposed on an otherwise straight base line, the integrator must be set to start measuring the peak only after the signal has exceeded the maximum deviation obtained with only carrier gas flowing. Thus the

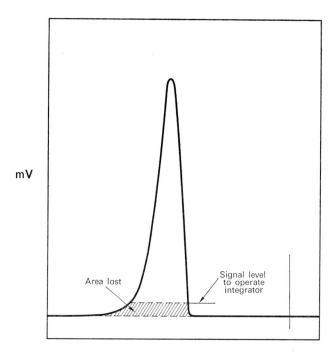

FIG. 45. Loss of signal from an integrator operating above base level.

widest part of the peak will not be measured. Reproducibility can be good but the area measurement can still be significantly in error (Fig. 45).

Although the peak areas, or the integrated response is a measure of quantity, the relation between this measurement and concentration of the component is not always a linear one. For this reason, the detector response must usually be calibrated in the range for which it is to be used. Whenever a calibration of this type is being made, area measurements of the differential response can well be replaced by the linear measure of the peak height, which is much easier and much more convenient to make. The departure from linearity of the peak height response is always greater than the corresponding departure of the peak area response. However, provided that the sample aliquots used are small (i.e. of the order of 0·5 ml or less), the departures from linearity are not excessive. Typical of such calibrations is that for carbon dioxide shown in Fig. 46.

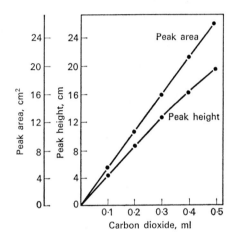

FIG. 46. Peak area and peak height calibrations for carbon dioxide. Column: 18 in. silica gel; carrier gas: hydrogen; bridge current: 300 mA.

The greatest sensitivity to any particular component is obtained by using the shortest possible column that will give the required separation. The sample aliquot should also be contained in the smallest possible column volume—it has already been noted that the by-pass sample injectors have been designed with this in mind—and should also be admitted to the chromatograph in a position immediately before the column.

It is often necessary to determine components present as minor constituents at the same time as components present in major proportion, during the course of a single-chromatographic run. The recorder sensitivity necessary to obtain a reasonable response for the minor constituents will often result in peaks for the major components that are many times greater than the full-scale deflection of the recorder. This is particularly so when a katharometer detector is used for the analysis of gaseous mixtures containing appreciable quantities of hydrogen. A common way of measuring such large peak responses is to reduce the proportion of the signal applied to the recorder. This is done, as in Fig. 27 (p. 43), by applying the signal from the detector to a chain of resistors, each of which is connected to the recorder via a suitable switch, *S*. This switch, used in conjunction with the sensitivity change switch *S2*, provides a means of rapidly changing the recorder sensitivity with ranges of 0–3, 0–5, 0–10, 0–15, 0–30, 0–50, 0–100, 0–150 and 0–300 mV full-scale deflection. When hydrogen is the main component of the sample mixture for analysis, a large measure of such attenuation is necessary to keep the peak on the chart as hydrogen gas has a thermal conductivity seven or eight times that of most other gases.

As an alternative to reducing the sensitivity of the recorder, the top portion of the chromatographic peak can be recorded by displacing the base line [122]. This is done by applying an accurately determined potential to the recorder in opposition to the output from the detector. This method results in a considerable gain in sensitivity, as may be seen from the following example of an actual analysis.

A gas sample containing about 40 % hydrogen was found to give a hydrogen response from a katharometer bridge circuit of about 115 mV, when a 1 ml aliquot was taken for analysis. This size of aliquot was selected in order to obtain a sensible peak measurement of the nitrogen present using the recorder at its maximum sensitivity of 3 mV full-scale deflection. In order to record the hydrogen peak, the signal was attenuated to about 2·3 mV, giving a peak height of 214·5 mm on the recorder trace. An error of 1 mm in the measurement of this peak height leads, therefore, to an inaccuracy of 0·5 % in the bridge signal.

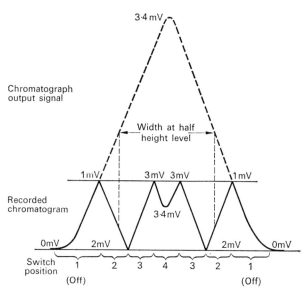

FIG. 47. Chromatogram obtained using a "fold over and zero displacement device". (Hamilton, *Analyt. Chem.* **34**, 445 (1962).)

By reducing the recorder sensitivity to 15 mV full-scale deflection and applying a potential of 21 mV in opposition to the bridge signal to the recorder (i.e. 105 × 3/15 mV), the recorder registered a signal of 10 mV (i.e. 115–105 mV), and gave a deflection of 186·4 mm. An error of 1 mm in the measurement of this response leads to an inaccuracy of only 0·05% in the bridge signal.

Backing-off devices of this nature are now available as optional features on some potentiometric recorders.

A somewhat similar device, that enables not only the position of the top of the peak to be noted, but also enables peak area measurements to be made, is a "fold over and zero displacement" device [123]. By means of a suitable electrical circuit, it can be arranged that when the recorder pen has completely traversed the chart, the signal from the bridge network is reversed in polarity, and at the same time a zero displacement potential equal to twice the recorder span is applied. The net effect is that of folding over the recorder trace (Fig. 47).

Calibration

The operation usually known as calibration is undertaken in order to relate the magnitude of the detector response to the concentration of the sample component causing it. It is usually a necessary step because, as noted above, the relation between the detector response and sample quantity (i.e. integral response and weight or volume of the component) is seldom linear over the whole of the concentration range used. Methods that are commonly used to relate response to sample quantity are summarized as follows.

Calculation from Physical Constants

The response of the gas-density balance and the ionization cross-section detectors can be related directly to the amount of sample component present provided that the molecular weight or ionization cross-section of the compound and of the carrier gas are known. Thus for the gas-density balance, provided that all the compounds present are eluted and correctly identified, the molecular weights can be calculated for substitution in the following equation:

$$\text{wt. } \% = \frac{100 \cdot F_n \cdot A_n}{\Sigma(F_n \cdot A_n)} \text{ (see p. 44)}$$

Classical Method

This method relies upon the preparation of special gas mixtures covering the concentration range of the sample for analysis. Each component is drawn from a suitable supply, isolated in a special vessel to enable its volume at constant pressure, or more often its pressure at constant volume to be determined prior to mixing. This method, although theoretically sound, is time consuming and tedious. As in some of the succeeding methods, the purity of the initial gas supplies should be established.

Use of Samples of Known Composition

Reference samples of known composition or of known gas content can be used to effect a calibration. This method is particularly important where the samples themselves are solid or liquid and can be preserved indefinitely. One example already noted [15] is that of using pure calcium carbonate to calibrate a katharometer for the determination of carbon dioxide in limestone.

Constant Volume Calibration Pipettes

These pipettes (Fig. 4, p. 11), for example, have a number of constant volume compartments that enable any of a number of sample sizes to be selected. These are used in conjunction with a supply of pure gas. Such devices have not found general favour as they are clumsy to install, use and maintain. Unless facilities are available for preparing special mixtures, they can be used for only one component at a time.

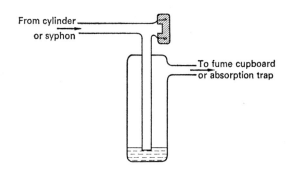

FIG. 48. Device for filling syringes with gas from a cylinder or syphon (Lodge, Pate and Huitt, *Chemist Analyst*, **52**, 53 (1963)).

Use of Syringe Pipette and By-pass Sample Loop

Standard mixtures can be prepared *in situ* using the by-pass injectors already described. The components are injected, one at a time, using a syringe pipette. This is not a suitable method for preparing standard mixtures containing many components, but is useful when it is possible to calibrate a detector for each constituent independently of the remainder.

A device for filling syringe pipettes with gas from a cylinder or syphon similar to that described by Lodge *et al.* [124], is shown in Fig. 48. It consists of a serum cap fitted to the input side of a gas bubbler containing mercury (not suitable for hydrogen sulphide) to give a slight positive pressure. Excess gas is removed to a fume duct or by using a suitable absorption vessel.

The Use of Gas Tubes

Gas tubes can be used for preparing standard mixtures of one component at high dilution in any other gas or gaseous mixture. The type of tube in which a serum cap is attached directly to the chamber of the tube, described on page 15, is the most suitable for this. Aliquots of sample mixtures prepared in this way can be removed through the serum cap and injected into a by-pass sample loop as described earlier.

Some gaseous mixtures cannot be prepared in this way because of physical adsorption of the component present in small amount upon the walls of the container. This has, for example, been observed during attempts to prepare sulphur dioxide–air mixtures containing parts per million of sulphur dioxide [125].

Gas-proportioning Pumps

These pumps, known also as gas-mixing pumps, can be used singly or coupled together to prepare calibration mixtures directly from cylinder supplies. Such pumps as, for example, those supplied by Messrs. Wosthoff o. H. G., can be used to prepare accurate dilutions of one gas in another, ranging from concentrations of near 100% to about 3000 ppm.

These pumps consist of two piston systems, each of single action, made from high grade resistant bronze. The pistons are driven by a common, self-starting synchronous motor, through a gear train which has interchangeable driving wheels. The gears and piston systems are immersed in an oil bath. Each piston is connected to an oil separating system to remove any minute droplets of oil from the gas mixture.

The operation of the pump is shown diagrammatically in Fig. 49. The driving wheels used to vary the mixing proportions are in a housing outside the main oil-filled compartment. Such pumps can be used in series to obtain three or more component mixtures, or to obtain greater dilutions than can be obtained with a single pump. In using two or more pumps, care must be taken that the total volume yield of each pump is greater than that required for the inlet of the succeeding pump.

The gases to be mixed should be of known purity, and must be introduced at constant pressure. By maintaining this known pressure, the maximum error in the mixing proportions is said by the manufacturers, to be no more than 0·2%.

Use of Permeation Tubes

For low concentrations, required, for example, for a primary standard in atmospheric pollution studies, use is made of gas permeation tubes. The required gas is sealed into a tube through which it can be permeated into a stream of inert gas used as diluent, often nitrogen. The rate of permeation can be determined by direct weighing. Permeation tubes have been prepared containing sulphur dioxide, nitrogen dioxide, water and some hydrocarbon gases [126].

Slow Injection Devices

Slow moving motor-driven syringes, as for example that described by Hill and Newell [127], can be used to obtain concentrations of volatile organic liquids at the parts per million level. The volatile liquid emerges from the syringe in the form of vapour, which is injected directly into an accurately metered stream of inert gas diluent.

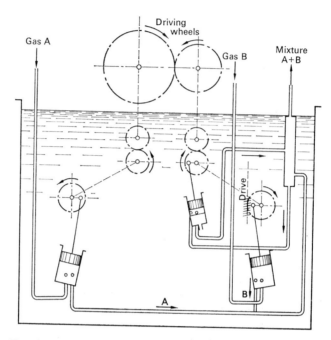

FIG. 49. Gas proportioning pump (Messrs. Wosthoff o.H.G.).

Recorders

The recorders used for gas chromatography should have a rapid response time and a full-scale deflection of no more than a few millivolts. Expensive models may also incorporate a backing-off, or zero displacement device and/or a sensitivity change mechanism.

For recorders that are in constant routine use, a number of small but useful improvements can be made. A foot-operated micro-switch that can be used to short the input terminals to the recorder has been found ideal for marking the recorder chart at the injection point when both hands are fully occupied. Such marking is not necessary for chromatographs using thermal conductivity cells, as the insertion of the sample results in a slight temporary displacement of the base line, but no similar indication is obtained when, for example, a flame ionization detector is in use.

The glass door panels can be removed and replaced with panels cut from acrylic sheet. This plastic panel can be cut away to allow the chart to pass through, or to permit identifying marks to be inscribed directly on the recorder chart.

Although potentiometric recorders are extensively used in gas chromatography, some of the earlier experiments were made using a simple millivolt meter to record the out-of-balance potential of a detector bridge circuit. This technique is not suited to rapid routine analysis, but can be employed for demonstration purposes.

Cathode ray tubes with long persistence screens have been used to display chromatographic signals [42]. This form of display is suitable only when it is possible to perform the required separation in a very short space of time. The time base of the cathode ray tube can be synchronized with the operation of the sample inlet mechanism, and the sample analysis completed within the period of the sweep time.

PART II

The Determination of Individual Gases

CHAPTER 7

Hydrogen

THE use of gas–solid chromatography for the separation of gaseous compounds has been established for a sufficient length of time for certain column packings to have become regarded as "standard" for particular applications. Thus, for example, columns packed with charcoal in a suitably activated form are in general use for the specific separation of oxygen from hydrogen. What is often overlooked in such generalizations is that the ability for a given separation to be undertaken on any particular column packing material is a function not only of the relative retention times or volumes, but also of the relative concentration of the components, of the sample size and of the order of elution from the column. Thus in the example given, no difficulty is encountered in separating small quantities of hydrogen from a large excess of oxygen, but the converse process, that of separating small quantities of oxygen from an excess of hydrogen, requires a much more careful selection of conditions.

In general, chromatographic separations are improved by reducing the size of the aliquot taken for analysis. In doing this, the detector must be selected so as to give sufficient sensitivity for all the required components in the reduced sample aliquot. Sufficient sensitivity in this context means giving a sufficiently large detector response to enable the required precision to be obtained. In the example quoted, quite small aliquots of the sample mixture can be used if the minor or trace constituent is hydrogen, as even a simple thermal conductivity cell has ample sensitivity to it. But for trace amounts of oxygen, no such reduction of the sample size is possible.

Where more than adequate separation can readily be obtained, and where a highly-sensitive detector can be used (as for example a micro-katharometer), then it is possible to combine reduction in sample size with an increase in speed of the analysis. This can be done by shortening the length of the chromatographic column, by increasing the temperature of operation or by increasing the carrier gas flow rate, or by a combination of these changes.

Separation of Hydrogen

The limit of detection of any particular gas depends not only upon the detector response to it, but also upon its position in the chromatogram in relation to the major constituents of the sample. As a general rule, minor constituents are more readily determined when they are eluted from a chromatographic column prior to the major constituents. No difficulty, therefore, arises in determining trace amounts of hydrogen, which are eluted before all other common gases from columns packed with silica gel, charcoal or molecular sieves—the three materials commonly used for the separation of the permanent gases. In general there is no advantage to be gained in using porous polymers if only hydrogen is to be determined.

Hydrogen, oxygen and nitrogen are eluted together from columns packed with alumina, and such columns are unsuitable for the separation of these or other permanent gases at room temperatures. If the determination of hydrogen is the only measurement to be made, then a 6–7 ft (2 m) length of column packed with

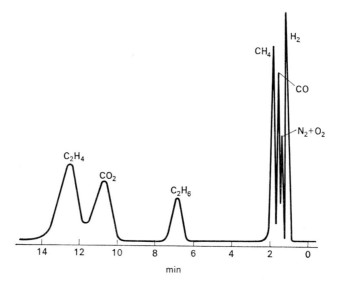

FIG. 50. Chromatogram of towns' gas (Boreham and Marhoff, Gas Council Research Communication No. GC 54). Column: 2 m 40–60 mesh silica gel; sample size: 5 ml; carrier gas: argon, 3·6 l/hr; temperature 30°; bridge voltage 5·0 V.

silica gel can be used at room temperature with argon or nitrogen as the carrier gas [128]. A chromatogram obtained using such a column for the analysis of towns' gas is shown in Fig. 50. For this determination a temperature of 30° was used, with argon as carrier gas at a flow rate of 3·6 l per hour.

If both hydrogen and oxygen are to be determined, then the choice of column packing material and of the experimental conditions will depend very much upon the relative amounts of hydrogen and oxygen present. If oxygen is the major component, the separation of both of these gases present in a 1 ml sample aliquot can be achieved quite easily using a similar length (2 m) of column packed with molecular sieve No. 5A and operating at room temperature. Either a thermal conductivity cell or a gas-density balance can be used as the detector. The former is simpler to use and just as effective as the latter. If the separation of hydrogen, argon and oxygen is required, the argon commonly used as carrier gas is replaced with nitrogen, and the chromatographic column packed with molecular sieve material is operated at a temperature of $-78°$. If the sample for analysis is composed largely of hydrogen, then the separation from oxygen is best made using a column packed with activated charcoal. As oxygen and nitrogen are not resolved on charcoal columns of average length, nitrogen is used as the carrier gas.

If the determination of hydrogen, oxygen and nitrogen are all required in these samples where hydrogen is the major constituent, then argon is used as the carrier gas and the column packed with activated charcoal is preceded or followed by a second column packed with molecular sieve. Carbon monoxide is eluted after methane from columns packed with molecular sieve, but before it from columns packed with activated charcoal. If the analytical requirement includes the determination of either of these two gases, then care must be taken to ensure that carbon monoxide and methane are not eluted together from the activated charcoal-molecular sieve column combination selected. Any carbon dioxide or water vapour present in these samples will be retained by the molecular sieve part of the chromatographic column. A short pre-column unit packed with potassium hydroxide followed by anhydrous magnesium perchlorate can, however, be used to remove both carbon dioxide and water vapour and thereby prolong the life of the column.

No difficulty is experienced in separating hydrogen from any of the organic gases. A short length of column packed with molecular sieve No. 5A is most effective for this.

Under normal chromatographic conditions, helium and neon are not separated from hydrogen and these two gases will, if present, be reported as hydrogen. A separation of these three gases can be made on long lengths of column packed with molecular sieve No. 5A by operating at low temperatures. Baum [129] has reported the separation of hydrogen from helium on a 12-ft column packed with molecular sieve 5A, at room temperature.

Detection of Hydrogen

The very large difference in thermal conductivity between hydrogen and argon or nitrogen has already been noted in Table 6. As a consequence of this, all designs of katharometer detector have exceptional sensitivity to hydrogen when argon or nitrogen are used as carrier gas. The large difference in density between hydrogen and argon leads also to a similar exceptional sensitivity of the gas-density balance to hydrogen, using argon as carrier. The sensitivity of these two detectors is sufficient for most practical applications, and generally there is little need for more complex detectors for the determination of hydrogen. When using either of these two, it is possible to detect and determine as little as 2×10^{-2} μl of hydrogen, which, in a 1 ml sample aliquot, corresponds to a concentration of 20 ppm.

The use of helium as carrier gas cannot be recommended for the determination of hydrogen, where either hot wire or thermistor model thermal conductivity cells are employed. It has been noted by Madison [130] that the sensitivity for the detection of hydrogen with helium as carrier gas is low because of the small difference in the thermal conductivities of the two gases. In addition, the determination is complicated by the anomalous cell response to hydrogen–helium mixtures. At high concentrations of hydrogen, the detector response is in the direction that would be predicted from the known values of the thermal conductivities of the two elements. As the amount of hydrogen in the helium carrier gas is reduced, the response of the detector gradually changes in direction, giving peaks similar in shape to those shown in Fig. 51. These chromatographic peaks were obtained by Madison using a Gow-Mac thermal conductivity cell, after separation of the hydrogen on a 25 ft length of column packed with charcoal. Madison attributed this unusual behaviour to the existence of a minimum value in the thermal conductivity curve for hydrogen–helium mixtures. The extent of this inversion of response will depend upon factors that affect the hydrogen concentration in the detector chamber, such as the absorbent used, cell geometry and sensing volume, column length and temperature of operation.

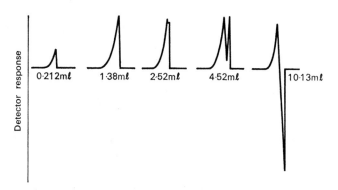

FIG. 51. Anomalous response of thermal conductivity cell to hydrogen–helium mixtures (Madison, *Analyt. Chem.* **30**, 1859 (1958)). Carrier gas: helium; sample gas: hydrogen.

This anomalous response can be avoided by measuring not the hydrogen content of the sample under investigation, but the water content, formed from the hydrogen in an oxidation stage. This oxidation can be effected quite easily by passing the gases eluted from the chromatographic column through a short length of tube packed with copper oxide and maintained at the appropriate temperature as described by Moore and Ward [131]. This procedure also results in an increased sensitivity to hydrogen, as the thermal conductivity difference between helium and water is very much greater than that between helium and hydrogen. If it is necessary (in order to obtain high sensitivities for the other constituents) to use a high-thermal conductivity gas in the determination of hydrogen, then a carrier gas consisting of 8 % hydrogen in helium gives a linear response to the hydrogen content of the mixture.

The flame thermocouple detector requires the use of hydrogen, either as carrier gas, or as a secondary gas supply in order to provide the flame necessary for this detector to operate. For this reason the flame thermocouple cannot be used to determine hydrogen as a component of sample mixtures. Partly for this reason, and partly because the gas from a jet of burning hydrogen is not appreciably ionized, the flame ionization detector is also not applicable to the determination of hydrogen. The extent of the ionization that does occur in a hydrogen flame can be gauged from the small standing current across a conventional flame ionization detector prior to commencing an analysis.

Ionization detectors have not been used extensively for the determination of hydrogen, largely because these detectors are, as a group, relatively insensitive to all the permanent gases. One exception to this is the helium ionization detector developed by Berry [96]. As only very small quantities of the gas sample are required, this detector is particularly useful where the quantity of the sample

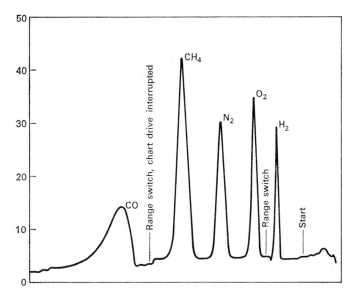

FIG. 52. Chromatogram of coal gas–air mixture (Berry, *Proc. 4th Symp. Gas Chromatog.*, Hamburg, 1962). Detector voltage: 750 V; column: 120 mm molecular sieve No. 5A; temperature: 100°; carrier gas: helium, 65 ml/min.

available is severely limited. This small size of sample aliquot not only gives improved chromatographic resolution, but also ensures extensive use of the molecular sieve column packing, before regeneration becomes necessary.

The chromatogram shown in Fig. 52, after Berry [18], shows the detection of $3 \times 10^{-3} \, \mu$l of hydrogen using this ionization detector. The limit of detection would appear to be about one-tenth of this value, i.e. $3 \times 10^{-4} \, \mu$l. Since hydrogen is the first peak to be eluted from any chromatographic column, large samples of at least 1 ml can be added without interference from any other constituent present in the sample. In this size of sample aliquot, the limit of detection corresponds to a concentration of 0·3 ppm of hydrogen, a figure confirmed by Wiseman [95].

Rhodes [132] has developed an automatic process chromatograph for the determination of 1–100 ppm of hydrogen in helium in which he uses a sub-divided charcoal column. Nitrogen carrier gas sweeps the sample from the sample loop onto the charcoal column and after the first pass the hydrogen would appear as a sharp peak on the trailing edge of the helium peak. When approximately 50% of the helium has passed the detector, a valve is turned which traps and then turns the hydrogen back through the first part of the column and subsequently also through the second and thence onto the detector. Thus the sample reaching the detector is richer in hydrogen and therefore better separated from the helium. The first part of the column is 48 ft and the second portion 12 ft in length. They are separated from each other by two internal passages of a 10-port rotary valve which allows the reversal of carrier gas at the appropriate time.

The conditions that have been used for the determination of hydrogen are summarized in the following examples, where the retention data of the separated gaseous compounds are also recorded.

EXAMPLE 1

Column dimensions	length 6 ft, internal diameter 0·125 in.
Packing	molecular sieve No. 5A, 36–52 mesh, activated for 3 hr at 350°
Temperature	35° (column and detector)
Carrier gas	argon, 30 ml/min
Detector	Gow-Mac hot wire thermal conductivity cell, type TE II
Recorder	3 mV f.s.d.
Sample	1 ml Fischer–Tropsch process residual gas
Retention times	hydrogen 1·5 min
	oxygen not separated
	nitrogen 4·5 min
	methane 7·0 min
	carbon monoxide 20·0 min
Reference	Warren Spring Laboratory [133]

EXAMPLE 2

Column dimensions	length 6 ft, internal diameter 0·125 in.
Packing	charcoal, 36–52 mesh, activated by heating for 2 hr at 250°
Temperature	35° (column and detector)
Carrier gas	argon, 30 ml/min
Detector	Gow-Mac hot wire thermal conductivity cell, type TE II
Recorder	3 mV f.s.d.
Sample	1 ml Fischer–Tropsch process residual gas
Retention times	hydrogen 2·0 min
	oxygen and nitrogen 4·0 min
	carbon monoxide 5·5 min
	methane 11·0 min
Reference	Warren Spring Laboratory [133]

EXAMPLE 3

Column dimensions	length 11 ft, internal diameter 0·125 in.
Packing	molecular sieve 3 ft, as in Example 1, with charcoal 8 ft as in Example 2
Temperature	35° (column and detector)
Carrier gas	argon, 30 ml/min
Detector	Gow-Mac hot wire thermal conductivity cell, type TE II
Recorder	3 mV f.s.d.
Sample	1 ml Fischer–Tropsch process residual gas

Retention times	hydrogen	2·2 min
	oxygen	4·0 min
	nitrogen	5·0 min
	carbon monoxide	10·1 min
	methane	13·2 min
Reference	Warren Spring Laboratory [133]	

These three examples illustrate the advantage gained in the separation of hydrogen, oxygen and nitrogen in hydrogen-rich gases, by using a combination of two columns packed with molecular sieve and charcoal respectively.

EXAMPLE 4

Column dimensions	length 4 m, internal diameter 4 mm
Packing	silica gel, 40–60 mesh
Temperature	30°
Carrier gas	argon 3·6 l./hr
Detector	Thermal conductivity cell, thermistor model
Sample	5 ml towns' gas
Retention times	hydrogen 1·5 min
	oxygen and nitrogen 1·8 min
	carbon monoxide 2·1 min
	methane 2·8 min
	ethane 10·5 min
	carbon dioxide 15·5 min
	ethylene 17·5 min
Reference	Boreham and Marhoff [128]

EXAMPLE 5

Column dimensions	*
Packing	109 g molecular sieve*
Temperature	22°
Carrier gas	argon, 30 ml/min
Detector	thermal conductivity cell
Retention times	helium 5·5 min
	neon 6·8 min
	hydrogen 8·0 min
Reference	Krejci *et al.* [120]

* At a packing density of 0·8 g/ml, this would represent a column 56 ft in length if packed into a tube of 0·125 in. internal diameter.

EXAMPLE 6

Column dimensions	length 120 cm, internal diameter 5 mm
Packing	molecular sieve No. 5A, 36–60 mesh, activated at 400°
Temperature	100° (column only, detector at room temperature)
Carrier gas	helium, 65 ml/min
Detector	helium ionization, anode potential 750 V
Sample	$1·6 \times 10^{-5}$ ml of coal gas–air mixture
Relative retention volumes	neon 1·0
	hydrogen 1·1
	oxygen 2·0
	argon 2·0
	nitrogen 3·4

EXAMPLE 6 (*cont.*)

Relative retention	krypton	4·0
volumes (*cont.*)	methane	5·0
	carbon monoxide	10·0
	xenon	13·8
Reference	Berry [18]	

Separation of the Isotopes and Isomers of Hydrogen

The use of gas chromatography for the separation of the hydrogen isotopes was first described by Glueckauf and Kitt [134] who used a displacement technique, and a column containing palladium. This early work stimulated efforts to find a suitable adsorbent to enable elution chromatography to be used as an alternative to the mass spectrographic methods then in common use for the determination of the hydrogen isotopes.

The first successful attempts were made by Ohkoshi *et al.* [135] and also by Reidel and Uhlmann [136], who used hydrogen (protium) as the carrier gas, and columns packed with molecular sieve No. 5A maintained at the temperature of liquid nitrogen. Deuterium (D_2) and protium deuteride (HD) were determined, and the protium obtained by difference. Using the same column material, a temperature of $-160°$, and helium as the carrier gas, Gant and Yang [137] succeeded in separating the spin isomers, ortho- and para-protium, and also protium tritide (HT) and tritium (T_2).

The separation of the spin isomers of protium, and the partial separation of the isomers of deuterium were also reported by Moore and Ward [131], who used a 120 cm length of column packed with activated alumina, a temperature of $-196°$, and helium as the carrier gas. The hydrogen was oxidized to water to avoid the difficulties usually encountered with helium–hydrogen mixtures when thermal conductivity cells are used as chromatographic detectors.

A column packed with a solid adsorbent containing both alumina and chromic oxide was used by Smith and Hunt [121] to separate protium, protium deuteride and deuterium. The column used was 12 ft in length, maintained at a temperature of $-196°$, and operated with neon as the carrier gas. The very long retention times that were noted with this column could be reduced somewhat by adding water to the column in order to produce a partial deactivation of the packing material. The same authors [121] later reported the separation of deuterium and protium deuteride on a column packed with silica gel, and showed that very little separation could be obtained when charcoal was used as the adsorbent material.

Separations with very much shorter retention times were described by Venugopalan and Kutschke [138] and by Phillips and Owens [139], both using helium as carrier gas and columns 6 ft in length, the former packed with activated alumina giving the separation shown in Fig. 53, and the latter packed with a mixture of alumina and ferric oxide but giving a similar separation.

When molecular sieve material is used as the column packing, *ortho*-protium and protium deuteride are eluted together, in the elution order *para*-protium, *ortho*-protium with protium deuteride and then deuterium. This elution order is also obtained from columns packed with alumina unless, as shown by Moore and

Ward [131], the packing material is strongly activated when it then results in the *ortho–para* conversion of the protium taking place on the column.

This conversion of *ortho-* to *para*-protium was also obtained by Furuyama and Kwan [140] using a column packed with activated alumina that had been coated with ferric oxide. This column 50 cm in length, was used in conjunction with a

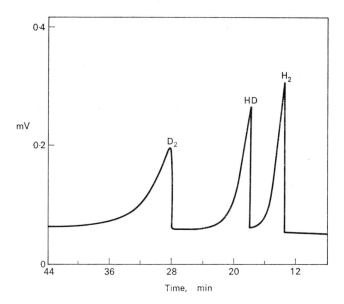

FIG. 53. Separation of protium, protium deuteride and deuterium (Venugopalan and Kutschke, *Canad. J. Chem.* **41,** 548 (1963)). Column: 6 ft strongly activated alumina; carrier gas: helium, 100 ml/min; temperature: −196°

column 200 cm in length, containing only activated alumina. Both columns were maintained at a temperature of −196°. At this temperature the *ortho*-protium of the composite peak obtained from the alumina column, was converted to *para*-protium during passage through the alumina–ferric oxide column. A complete separation of the spin isomers, protium deuteride and deuterium was thereby obtained.

One of the most elegant ways yet described for obtaining a complete separation of the hydrogen isotopes and isomers was described by Mohnke and Saffert [43] using a gas–solid capillary column for the separation of *para*-protium, *ortho*-protium, protium deuteride, *para*-deuterium and *ortho*-deuterium which were eluted in that order from a glass column, the inside of which had been coated with an active form of silica (for preparation of this column, see p. 35). Neon was used as the carrier gas, and a micro-thermal conductivity cell as the detector. The separation achieved is shown in Fig. 54. The helium response was taken to represent the dead time of the capillary column.

This work was followed by that of Cercy *et al.* [141], who obtained a very rapid separation of protium, protium deuteride and deuterium on a long length of narrow-bore pyrex glass tubing packed with 100–200 micron size activated alumina particles. A temperature of −196° was used, with helium as the carrier gas and a micro-thermal conductivity cell as detector—this time of the thermistor pattern.

For the detection of tritium the micro-thermal conductivity cell used to record the presence of the other two isotopes of hydrogen, is replaced with or supplemented by a low-energy β-radiation detector. A vibrating reed electrometer equipped with high resistance lead [142] has been used for this purpose. Other detectors include a suitable quenched Geiger–Muller flow counter [143] and an anthracene crystal scintillation counter [144]. For measurement of very low tritium activities Karmen et al. [145] have used a series of cartridges each containing p-terphenyl crystals coated with silicone oil. One cartridge was used for each frac-

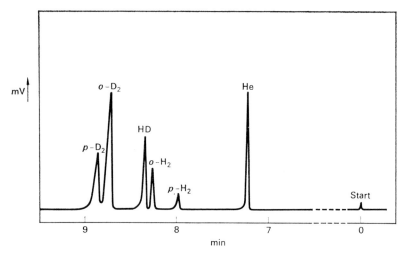

FIG. 54. Separation of hydrogen isotopes and their spin isomers (Mohnke and Saffert, *Proc. 4th Symp. Gas Chromatog.*, Hamburg, 1962). Column length 80 m; temperature: −196°; carrier gas: neon, 2 ml/min; sample size 1·5 μl.

tion collected. On collection, each cartridge was transferred to a vial containing diphenyloxazole in toluene, and the vial and contents placed in a liquid scintillation counter.

The separation of the hydrogen isotopes including tritium, was described by Phillips and Owens [139], using a column packed with alumina and ferric oxide. Helium was used as carrier gas, and the retention times were given as

Protium	15·0 min
protium tritide	20·0 min
deuterium	21·5 min
tritium	27·0 min

Carter [146] and Smith and Carter [142] describe the use of a column 8 ft in length packed with alumina activated at a temperature of 370°, with helium as carrier gas and a column temperature of −196° to obtain an absolute resolution of protium, protium tritide and tritium (Fig. 55) and also deuterium, deuterium tritide and tritium. Using neon as carrier gas they also obtained an adequate separation of protium, protium tritide, deuterium, deuterium tritide and tritium. Activation of the packing at 350° for 53 hr and increasing the column length to a total of 12 ft, produced an improvement in the resolution of the isotopes when protium was used as carrier, but when helium or neon were used, the various isotopes were not eluted in reasonable retention times.

Separations of protium, protium tritide and tritium were also reported by Carter [146] and by Smith and Carter [142] on columns packed with silica gel, alumina with chromic oxide, and alumina with ferric oxide.

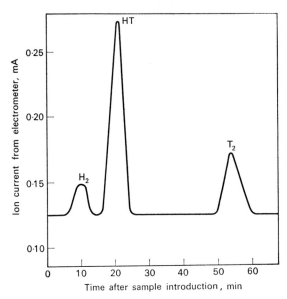

Fig. 55. Electrometer trace showing the separation of protium, protium tritide and tritium (Smith and Carter, in *Tritium in the Physical and Biological Sciences*, I.A.E.A., Vienna). Column: 8 ft, 80–100 mesh-activated alumina; carrier gas: helium, 65 ml/min; temperature −196°.

The separation of protium, protium deuteride, protium tritide, deuterium, deuterium tritide and tritium has been reported by West and Marston [147] and by Genty and Schott [148] at −196° also on a column of alumina covered with ferric oxide.

EXAMPLE 7

Column dimensions	length 120 cm, internal diameter 5 mm
Packing	alumina, 150–200 mesh
Temperature	−196°
Carrier gas	helium, 240 ml/min
Detector	thermal conductivity cell, used after conversion of the hydrogen to water
Sample size	1·5 ml
Retention times	*para*-protium 4·5 min
	ortho-protium 5·5 min
Reference	Moore and Ward [131]

EXAMPLE 8

Column dimensions	length 12 ft
Packing	chromic oxide–alumina*
Temperature	−196°
Carrier gas	neon, 35 ml/min
Detector	thermal conductivity cell
Retention times	protium 114 min†
	protium deuteride 133 min
	deuterium 200 min
Reference	Smith and Hunt [121]

* This material was prepared by adding 6·7% by weight of chromium trioxide in 350 ml of water to 225 g of 20–40 mesh alumina and agitating for 3 hr. The excess liquid was removed by filtration and the residue dried. The chromium trioxide was then reduced in hydrogen at a temperature of 360°. Small dust particles were removed by screening, and the remaining material used to pack the chromatographic column. After packing, the column material was partially deactivated by adding water.

† On partial deactivation, the retention times were reduced to protium 90 min, protium deuteride 100 min, deuterium 130 min.

EXAMPLE 9

Column packing	silica gel, activated at 140–150°
Temperature	−196°
Carrier gas	protium, 144 ml/min
Detector	thermal conductivity cell
Retention times	protium deuteride 42 min
	deuterium 50 min
Reference	Smith and Hunt [121]

EXAMPLE 10

Column dimensions	length 8 m, internal diameter 0·27 mm
Packing	silica, 20 micron layer on wall of tubing (see p. 35)
Temperature	−196°
Carrier gas	neon 2 ml/min
Sample size	1·5 μl
Detector	micro-thermal conductivity cell
Retention times	*para*-protium 8·0 min
	ortho-protium 8·2 min
	protium deuteride 8·3 min
	ortho-deuterium 8·8 min
	para-deuterium 8·9 min
Reference	Mohnke and Saffert [43]

EXAMPLE 11

Column dimensions	length 19 m, internal diameter 0·4 mm
Packing	alumina, chromatographic grade CBT 1, 100–120 micron size
Temperature	−196°
Carrier gas	helium
Detector	thermal conductivity cell, thermistor model
Sample size	0·025 ml
Retention volumes	"dead volume" 24 ml
	protium 42 ml
	protium deuteride 52 ml
	deuterium 64 ml
Reference	Cercy *et al.* [141]

EXAMPLE 12

Column dimensions	length 8 ft
Packing	alumina, 80–100 mesh, activated at a temperature of 370° for 8 hr under flowing helium
Temperature	−196°
Carrier gas	helium
Detector	50 ml Borkowski ionization chamber with a Cary Model 31 vibrating reed electrometer

Retention times	protium	10 min
	protium tritide	20 min
	tritium	54 min
Reference	Smith and Carter [142]	

EXAMPLE 13

Column dimensions	length 3 m
Packing	deactivated alumina–ferric oxide 125–150 microns
Temperature	−196°
Carrier gas	neon
Detector	thermal conductivity cell and/or ionization chamber

Retention times	protium	14 min
	protium deuteride	16 min
	protium tritide	18 min
	deuterium	22 min
	deuterium tritide	25 min
	tritium	30 min
Reference	Genty and Schott [148]	

EXAMPLE 14

Column dimensions	length 2 m, internal diameter 2 mm
Packing	molecular sieve 4A, 0·16–0·25 mm, activated at 500° under vacuum
Temperature	−149°
Carrier gas	28 ml/min helium
Detector	thermal conductivity cell

Retention times	protium	20 min
	protium deuteride	25 min
	protium tritide	29 min
	deuterium	35 min
	deuterium tritide	40 min
	tritium	44 min
Reference	Centi and Lesimple [149]	

CHAPTER 8

The Noble Gases

Helium, Neon, Argon, Krypton and Xenon

The five gases of this group are characterized by an almost complete lack of chemical reactivity, and for this reason physical methods have always been employed for their determination. Known also as the "rare" or "inert" gases, they are by no means as rare or as unimportant as is often supposed. In air, for example, argon is present to an extent of 0.94%, being more abundant than carbon dioxide, and next in abundance after oxygen. All five gases have important commercial applications.

The greatest difficulty involved in making a chromatographic separation of all five of these gases from each other, is that of resolving neon and helium. Janak [150] has reported that at a temperature of $20°$, with carbon dioxide as carrier gas and using a 2.5 m length of column packed with activated charcoal, a good resolution of helium, argon, krypton and xenon can be obtained, but any neon present is eluted with the helium. The separation of argon, krypton and xenon from each other has also been obtained using columns packed with silica gel maintained at a temperature of $23°$ by Greene [151], and with columns packed with molecular sieve No. 5A at a temperature of $100°$, by Berry [18].

Of more importance than the resolution of mixtures of the noble gases is the separation of individual members of the group from other more common gases with similar retention times, such as helium–neon–hydrogen, argon–oxygen, krypton–nitrogen and xenon–carbon monoxide. Each of these groups being eluted either as a single composite peak, or as incompletely resolved peaks from columns packed with molecular sieve, a material frequently used for the separation of the more common gaseous compounds. From columns packed with molecular sieve, krypton is eluted on the trailing edge of the nitrogen response, and xenon on the trailing edge of the carbon monoxide response. It is therefore easier to detect xenon in air than it is to detect similar amounts of krypton. Conversely, it is easier to detect krypton in the presence of excess carbon monoxide than it is to detect xenon in the same gas.

Where difficulties of this nature do arise, the separation can often be improved by the usual devices of increasing the column length, reducing the carrier gas flow rate and lowering the temperature of the column. Where overlapping peaks are obtained, it is sometimes possible to use one of the two components as the carrier gas for the determination of the other. Thus oxygen and argon are eluted almost simultaneously at room temperature from columns packed with molecular sieve, but can be resolved by using very long columns, or by operating at low temperatures. Provided that the determination of oxygen is not required, then a measure of the argon content of sample mixtures can be obtained by using oxygen as the carrier gas as described by Greene [151]. Similarly, helium can be used as carrier gas when the determination of neon is required, and nitrogen when krypton is wanted.

Hydrogen can also be used as carrier gas for the determination of helium, but the difficulties involved in using a thermal conductivity cell for the analysis of helium–hydrogen mixtures (see p. 86) must not be overlooked. A more satisfactory way of determining helium in the presence of hydrogen is to use a long column to obtain a

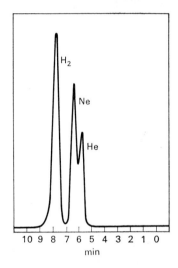

FIG. 56. Separation of hydrogen, neon and helium (Krejci, Tesarik and Janak, *Gas Chromatography, Instr. Soc. Amer. Symp.* 1959, Academic Press). Column: molecular sieve No. 5A; temperature: 22°; carrier gas: argon 0·5 ml/sec.

complete separation of the two gases. Phillips and Owens [139], for example, used a 15 ft length of column packed with molecular sieve No. 5A, for this separation. Argon was used as the carrier gas, and the column was operated at room temperature. The limit of detection, using a thermal conductivity cell, was given as less than 0·01% helium. Attempts to separate the isotopes of helium, He-3 and He-4 on a 20 ft length of column packed with molecular sieve were unsuccessful.

As an alternative to increasing the length of the chromatographic column, the temperature of operation can be lowered. The increased separation obtained in this way for mixtures of helium, neon and hydrogen by Krejci *et al.* [120] is shown in Fig. 56. The length of the column used was not stated, but at a packing density of 0·8 g/ml, the weight of material used would correspond to a column length of 56 ft if packed into a tube of $\frac{1}{8}$ in. internal diameter.

The separation of argon from oxygen cannot be accomplished satisfactorily at room temperature. As an alternative to using oxygen as the carrier gas when the determination of argon is required, hydrogen can be used and the oxygen present removed by catalytic combustion. This is easily achieved using a pre-column unit containing palladium metal supported on an inert material such as celite. Wilson *et al.* [152] introduced carbon tetrafluoride on firebrick at $-183°C$ to effect the separation of argon and oxygen on a 15 ft column which permitted the separation of these two gases from each other and from nitrogen in less than 10 min. Havlena and Hutchinson [153] used a composite three-part column at 110° to separate these gases; the three sections of column consisting of 9 ft of molecular sieve 5A activated at 350° for 1 hr, 3 ft of 80–100 mesh Porapak T followed by an intermediate column consisting of a 1 ft length of 80–100 mesh Porapak A coated with palladium chloride. The intermediate section was coated by evaporating 50 ml of 10:1 acetone: hydrochloric acid containing 1·5 g $PdCl_2$ with 7 g Porapak Q. The com-

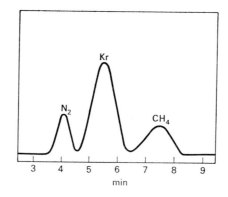

FIG. 57. Separation of nitrogen, krypton and methane (Krejci, Tesarik and Janak, *Gas Chromatography, Instr. Soc. Amer. Symp.* 1959, Academic Press). Column: molecular sieve and charcoal.

bined column was heated at 180° with hydrogen flowing until the palladium chloride was fully reduced; hydrogen at 95 ml/sec was used as carrier gas; the retention times were argon 2 min, nitrogen 3 min, and oxygen (as water) 5 min.

Krypton is eluted with methane from columns packed with activated charcoal, and with nitrogen from columns packed with molecular sieve No. 5A. By combining charcoal with molecular sieve, the elution of krypton can be obtained at intermediate positions between these two other gases. Figure 57, from Krejci *et al.* [120], shows the elution of krypton from a column packed with charcoal and molecular sieve mixed in the ratio 1:10.

As for other separations, the degree of activation of the solid absorbent is of considerable importance. Berry [18], for example, gives the retention time of krypton on a column packed with molecular sieve, relative to nitrogen, as 1·18; Krejci *et al.* [120] give a figure of 0·995 for the same separation, when the water content of the molecular sieve is 2% by weight.

For most of these applications a thermal conductivity cell has been used as detector: a gas-density balance would also serve to record any of these gases. The helium ionization detector developed by Berry [96] can be used for the determination of minor or trace amounts of neon, argon, krypton and xenon, though not, of course, of helium itself.

Purer [154] has described a procedure for the determination of impurities in gaseous helium in the parts per billion range. The impurities in the sample were concentrated by passing the helium through a trap at liquid helium temperature and then allowing the condensate to evaporate on to a 16 ft column packed with molecular sieve 13X. Neon, hydrogen, argon, oxygen, krypton, nitrogen, methane and xenon were detected by this means.

Liebenberg [155] has reported the quantitative determination of helium-3 using an 8 ft column of 0·18 in. i.d. filled with 24–50 mesh molecular sieve 5A, operated at 100°. Helium-4 had been passed through the column at 200° for activation, and was used as carrier gas; retention times of 2 min for helium-3, and 4 min for oxygen were reported.

EXAMPLE 1

(See Example 6, Chapter 7, p. 89.)

EXAMPLE 2

Packing	molecular sieve No. 5A, 109 g*	
Temperature	−78°	
Carrier gas	argon, 26·7 ml/min	
Detector	thermal conductivity cell	
Retention times	helium	7·0 min
	neon	8·8 min
Reference	Krejci *et al.* [120]	

* At a packing density of 0·8 g/ml, this weight would be contained in a column 56 ft in length, 0·125 in. internal diameter.

See also Example 5, Chapter 7, p. 89, where a separation of helium, neon and hydrogen is given using this column at a temperature of 22°.

EXAMPLE 3

Column packing	activated charcoal 1 part, with molecular sieve No. 5A, 10 parts	
Temperature	ambient	
Detector	thermal conductivity cell	
Retention times	nitrogen	4·0 min
	krypton	5·5 min
	methane	7·5 min
Reference	Krejci *et al.* [120]	

EXAMPLE 4

Column dimensions	length 2·5 ft, internal diameter 0·25 in.	
Packing	molecular sieve No. 5A, 30–70 mesh, activated for 1 hr at 300°	
Temperature	−72°	
Carrier gas	helium, 100 ml/min	
Detector	thermal conductivity cell	
Sample size	10 ml	
Retention times	argon	2·5 min
	oxygen	3·5 min
Reference	Lard and Horne [119]	

EXAMPLE 5

Column dimensions	length 10 ft, external diameter 0·25 in.
Packing	activated charcoal, 20–40 mesh
Temperature	−196°
Carrier gas	hydrogen, 60 ml/min
Detector	thermal conductivity cell
Retention volumes	helium 180 ml
	neon 360 ml
Reference	Greene [151]

EXAMPLE 6

Column dimensions	length 10 ft, external diameter 0·25 in.
Packing	silica gel (Davison), 20–40 mesh
Temperature	23°
Carrier gas	oxygen, 60 ml/min
Detector	thermal conductivity cell
Retention volumes	argon 150 ml
	krypton 240 ml
	xenon 840 ml
Reference	Greene [151]

EXAMPLE 7

Column dimensions	length 10 ft, external diameter 0·25 in.
Packing	molecular sieve No. 5A, 20–40 mesh
Temperature	23° to the elution of methane, then raised to 100° to elute xenon
Carrier gas	oxygen, 60 ml/min
Detector	thermal conductivity cell
Retention volumes	argon 160 ml
	krypton 540 ml
	methane 660 ml
	xenon 960 ml
Reference	Greene [151]

EXAMPLE 8

Column dimensions	length 15 ft, external diameter 0·25 in.
Packing	CF_4 on firebrick
Temperature	−183°
Carrier gas	helium
Detector	thermal conductivity cell
Sample size	5 ml
Retention times	nitrogen 3 min
	argon 5·5 min
	oxygen 9 min
Reference	Wilson *et al.* [152]

Other examples of the separation of the noble gases are given in the following papers:

ABEL, K. Determination of argon in the presence of oxygen and other atmospheric gases by adsorption chromatography. *Analyt. Chem.* **36,** 953 (1964).

BOURKE, P. J., DAWSON, R. W. and DENTON, W. H. Detection of volume parts per million of permanent gases in helium. *J. Chromatog.* **14,** 387 (1964).

JONES, K. and HALFORD, P. Separation and determination of argon and oxygen in high-purity nitrogen streams by gas chromatography. *Nature,* **202,** 1002 (1964).

KARLSSON, B. M. Determination of minute quantities of nitrogen in argon by gas chromatography. *Analyt. Chem.* **35,** 1311 (1963).

SWINNERTON, J. W., LINNENBOM, V. J. and CHEEK, C. H. Determination of argon and oxygen by gas chromatography. *Analyt. Chem.* **36,** 1669 (1964).

CHAPTER 9

Some Common Gases

Oxygen, Nitrogen, Methane, Carbon Monoxide and Carbon Dioxide

The separation and subsequent determination of the gases in this group have been the subject of more study than that of any other group except perhaps that of the hydrocarbon gases. This interest can be accounted for partly by the widespread use of gaseous mixtures containing all or most of these gases in varying proportions, often together with hydrogen, and partly by the commercial value of such mixtures and the need for rapid, accurate analyses on an ever-increasing scale. It is doubtful if any gas mixture or, indeed, the supply of any pure gas is entirely free of all five gases in this group.

Separation in this Group

No single chromatographic packing is known that can be used to effect a separation at room temperature of oxygen, nitrogen and carbon dioxide when present together in a gaseous mixture. In order to undertake the complete analysis of such mixtures it is necessary to use at least two column packings, although these can sometimes be arranged so as to require only a single detector.

The use of haemoglobin of human or animal blood has been suggested by Gil-av and Herzberg-Minzly [156], for the separation of oxygen from nitrogen. The blood is supported on firebrick and the column stored under helium when not in use. This separation has also been obtained using long lengths of column packed with suitably activated charcoal. Madison [130], for example, used a column 25 ft in length and obtained retention times of 13–15 min for oxygen and 15–18 min for nitrogen, with helium as the carrier gas.

More frequently used materials for this separation of oxygen from nitrogen are the molecular sieves. Of those commonly available, most work has been done with No. 5A. Rapid separations can be obtained on columns only a few feet in length and, provided always that the sample material is not composed very largely of hydrogen, good separations of hydrogen, oxygen, nitrogen, methane and carbon monoxide can be obtained; the gases being eluted in that order. Carbon dioxide is retained by the column packing material, and together with the retention of water vapour present in most gas samples, gives rise to a progressive deterioration of the molecular sieve material. This deterioration is generally observed as a gradual loss of the ability of such columns to separate oxygen from nitrogen.

For most applications the molecular sieve material is carefully sized, and a size fraction in the range 40–100 mesh is used. More recently Bombaugh [157] has described the use of molecular sieve flour for the separation of hydrogen, oxygen, nitrogen, methane and carbon monoxide. One part by weight of a molecular sieve No. 5A fraction passing a 200 mesh sieve was mixed with two parts by weight of 60–80 mesh red Chromosorb, rolled in a cylindrical container for 18 hr and then screened. The fine material was rejected and the 60–80 mesh fraction was used to pack the chromatographic column. Bombaugh observed that of the original 33% added, 28% of the molecular sieve was retained on the Chromosorb. Using such a column he obtained a sixfold increase in efficiency and an almost twofold increase in peak height compared with a column packed with 60–80 mesh material. This is illustrated in Fig. 58.

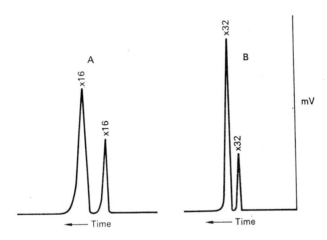

FIG. 58. Separation of oxygen from nitrogen using finely ground molecular sieve No. 5A on Chromosorb (Bombaugh, *Nature*, **197**, 1102 (1963)). A, 60–80 mesh molecular sieve: B, molecular sieve flour coated on Chromosorb.

Molecular sieve "powder" has been used successfully by Farré-Rius and Guiochon [158] to achieve the separation of oxygen, nitrogen, methane and carbon monoxide in 25 sec. These authors obtained a powder size of 315–400 microns by washing the molecular sieve with water and decanting the fine particles with the supernatant liquid. The powder was dried and activated at 400° and the column packed in the usual way. The 25-sec separation was obtained on a 200-cm column operated at 100° with hydrogen as carrier gas.

Another packing material used extensively for the separation of the gases in this group is activated charcoal. Ray [60] showed that columns packed with this material could be used for the separation of hydrogen, carbon monoxide and methane. Patton *et al*. [159] showed in addition the separation of carbon dioxide. Oxygen and nitrogen are not resolved on columns of average length used for these separations. A similar separation of hydrogen, oxygen plus nitrogen, carbon monoxide, methane and carbon dioxide can be obtained by using columns packed with silica gel, suitably activated. An example of latter separation described by Boreham and Marhoff [128], is given as Example 4, Chapter 7, p. 89.

Methane is eluted after carbon monoxide from columns packed with activated charcoal or silica gel, but before carbon monoxide from columns packed with molecular sieve. By using a combination of either charcoal or silica gel with molecular sieve, it is possible to select any retention time for either of these two components within the range given by the individual stationary phases. This combination of two columns has already been noted as a means of improving the separation of oxygen from hydrogen, but can also be used in the analysis of samples containing carbon monoxide, to decrease the retention time and hence increase the peak height response obtained for this component. This device is only necessary where the determination of both oxygen and nitrogen are also required, necessitating the use of some molecular sieve material. As noted previously, when preparing columns containing the two solid adsorbents, care must be taken to avoid combinations from which a composite peak is obtained for carbon monoxide and methane.

In the authors' laboratory, the determination of hydrogen, oxygen, nitrogen, carbon monoxide and methane is made from a single injection sample, using this column combination of molecular sieve and activated charcoal. Any carbon dioxide present is then determined from a separate sample injection using an additional column. Short columns packed with either silica gel or activated charcoal are the most convenient for this separation, but partition columns can also be used. Organic liquids that have been used as stationary phases for the separation of carbon dioxide from the remaining gases of this group include di-n-butyl-maleate, di-2-ethylhexylsebacate and hexamethylphosphoramide.

An alternative technique for the separation of carbon dioxide from the remaining gases of the group is that of temperature programming. This procedure, described by Graven [25], was used by W. G. Pye and Co. Ltd. to obtain the chromatogram shown in Fig. 59. Hydrogen, oxygen, nitrogen, and methane were all eluted at room temperature, and the carbon monoxide and carbon dioxide then eluted by heating at a rate of $10°/min$. Temperature programming cannot, however, be considered as an ideal technique where, as in routine gas analysis, the closest control must be maintained over the temperature used for the separation.

Molecular sieve packings are not ideal materials for temperature programmed separations as any water vapour absorbed by the column may then be removed as a broad elution band and obscure the elution of other components. Horton [160] has recommended that not only should such columns be dried at $250°$ before use, but should be maintained at this temperature for 30 min after each day's work, even when all analyses undertaken during that day were at room temperature. Two complete heating-cooling cycles are recommended before any sample is admitted to the column, and when not in use the column should be sealed.

Various systems have been devised to allow the separation of the common gases from each other and from other constituents using one detector and one sample aliquot. Some of these are mentioned in Chapter 15 ("Complete Gas Analysis"). A recent addition to these techniques is that described by Obermiller and Charlier [161] in which the sample is passed first to a 10 ft column packed with 50 to 80 mesh Porapak Q maintained at a temperature of $90°$ and thence to one side of a thermal conductivity cell. Nitrogen, oxygen, argon and carbon monoxide appear together as a single peak in 0·5 min, followed in order by carbon dioxide (1 min), hydrogen sulphide (2·5 min) and sulphur dioxide (5·75 min). While these separations and detections are being carried out, the composite peak is being separated on a second column, 20 ft long packed with Porapak Q held at a temperature of −70°, giving nitrogen (10 min from start), oxygen (12 min), argon (13 min) and carbon monoxide (16 min). Detection is made in the second arm of the thermal conductivity cell. Helium is used as carrier gas and electrical polarity is switched

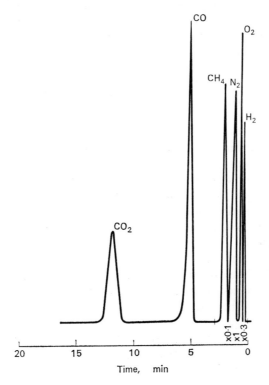

Fig. 59. Chromatogram of a mine gas (W. G. Pye & Co. Ltd.). Column: 2 ft molecular sieve No. 5A; detector: cross-section ionization; carrier gas: helium: room temperature for 3 min, then temperature programmed at 10°/min.

after the elution of sulphur dioxide, corresponding with the change of sensing arm of the cell. Systems employing multi column techniques have also been reported by Solomon [162], Manka [163] and by Terry and Futrell [164] who used a three-column, two-detector system for the simultaneous analysis of a mixture of permanent gases and hydrocarbons.

No difficulty is encountered in separating the gases of this group from the remaining hydrocarbon gases. Such hydrocarbon gases are eluted after methane from columns packed with either silica gel or activated charcoal. This separation can also be made using columns packed with molecular sieve material from which only branched chain hydrocarbons are eluted (plus methane).

Some interest has been shown in the separation of isotopes of some of these gases. Bocola *et al.* [165] obtained a separation of $^{18}O_2$ and $^{16}O_2$ at $-193°$ on passing through a 170 m, 0·28 mm i.d. column coated internally with a 10 micron thickness of silica. The silica layer was formed by etching the inner glass wall with a 20% NaOH solution for 6 hr at 100°, washing to neutralize the alkali and subsequently activating the silica by passing the carrier gas (nitrogen) for 48 hr at 200°. Detection was by electron capture and a 50 ml/min scavenger of nitrogen was employed.

Bruner and DiCorcia [166] separated $^{14}N_2$ and $^{15}N_2$ (retention times 477 and 495 min respectively) using a partially graphitized carbon black ("Graphon") in a 60 mm $\times$ 4 mm i.d. column at $-196°$ with a helium/carbon monoxide carrier gas. To avoid peak tailing the carbon black was treated with 1% of squalane. The carbon monoxide in the carrier gas acted as a further mobile deactivator of the stationary phase.

Carrier Gas

For most of these separations either argon or helium gas is used as carrier. The use of argon avoids the necessity of separating argon from oxygen, and the error involved in calculating the combined argon-plus-oxygen response as oxygen. Some improvement in sensitivity can be obtained by using hydrogen as the carrier gas in those analyses where hydrogen is not required.

This added sensitivity is particularly important in the determination of carbon dioxide when a thermal conductivity cell is used as the detector. The small difference in thermal conductivity results in a very poor sensitivity to carbon dioxide when argon is used as the carrier gas. Some small improvement can be obtained by using a gas-density balance as the detector, but the alternative choice, that of using hydrogen or helium as the carrier gas, is preferred.

Using either of these gases as carrier, it is possible to determine oxygen, nitrogen and carbon dioxide using a single thermal conductivity cell as detector, employing the two arms of the cells alternatively as the sensing and reference arms. This system has been used for the analysis of sewage sludge digester gas [167], described in more detail in Chapter 15. The gas sample is passed first to a short chromatographic column packed with silica gel, where a separation of carbon dioxide from all other gases takes place. The gases are passed to one arm of a thermal conductivity cell, the other arm containing pure hydrogen serving as the reference arm. The carbon dioxide is then removed by absorption in caustic alkali, and the remaining constituents of the sample separated on a column packed with molecular sieve No. 5A, before detection in the arm of the thermal conductivity cell previously used as the reference arm. A similar system has been described by Mortimer [168].

Detection

Most analyses of mixtures containing these common gases are made using thermal conductivity cells with either hot wire or thermistor elements as detectors. Gas-density balances can also be used for determining these gases when present in quantity or in minor amounts. Neither the thermal conductivity cell nor the gas-density balance are suitable for the determination of trace amounts except under favourable conditions. The circuit diagram of a gas chromatograph built for the express purpose of analysing mixtures of these common gases, all present in major or minor amounts, using a thermistor model gas-density balance, is shown in Fig. 29 (p. 46).

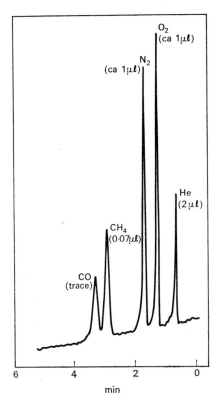

FIG. 60. Detection of some common gases with annular design of argon cell (Shahin and Lipsky, *Analyt. Chem.* **35**, 472 (1963)). Applied voltage: 1·34 V; carrier gas: argon; detector temperature: 165°.

Reference has already been made to the helium ionization detector of Berry [96], for the analysis of gaseous mixtures, and an example of an analysis made with this detector has already been given (Example 6, Chapter 7, p. 89). The highly sensitive ionization detector with concentric geometry, small chamber volume and low applied potential described by Shahin and Lipsky [93] has also been used for the detection of the gases in this group. The separation and detection of some gases using argon as carrier gas and presumably molecular sieve as column packing, is shown in Fig. 60.

The cross-section ionization detector [49] has also been used for the determination of the major constituents of mixtures of inorganic gases. In a latter, more sensitive form [87], it responds to very small quantities of the permanent gases, provided that they are present at high concentration in the sample material.

A device that can be used to improve the detection is to convert the compound of low sensitivity to one of higher sensitivity. Thus both carbon monoxide and carbon dioxide can be converted to methane by catalytic hydrogenation in the presence of reduced nickel [169], and the sensitive flame ionization detector then used to complete the determination.

EXAMPLES 1–5

(See Examples 1–4 and 6, Chapter 7, p. 89.)

EXAMPLE 6

Column dimensions	length 35 cm, internal diameter 4 mm
Packing	activated charcoal, 75–100 mesh
Temperature	40°
Carrier gas	nitrogen
Detector	katharometer
Retention times	hydrogen 2 min
	methane 3 min
	carbon dioxide 5 min
	ethylene 12 min
	ethane 17 min
Reference	Ray [60]

EXAMPLE 7

Chromatograph	Pye Panchromatograph
Column dimensions	length 2 ft
Packing	molecular sieve No. 5A
Temperature	room temperature for 3 min, then temperature programmed at 10°/min
Carrier gas	helium
Detector	cross-section ionization
Retention times	hydrogen 0·3 min
	oxygen 0·6 min
	nitrogen 1·5 min
	methane 2·5 min
	carbon monoxide 5 min
	carbon dioxide 12 min
Reference	Manufacturer's literature, W. G. Pye and Co. Ltd.

CHAPTER 10

The Hydrocarbon Gases

THE hydrocarbon gases are normal constituents of many gaseous mixtures, and their determination is a matter of some considerable commercial importance. The use of "natural gas" in place of the more familiar coal gas as a source of domestic fuel has led to the increased use of gas chromatography for the analysis of towns' gas, and in particular of the hydrocarbon fraction. The importance of the hydrocarbon fraction of engine exhaust gases, flue gases, sewer gas and many other gaseous mixtures has undoubtedly contributed to the rapid development of this aspect of gas chromatography.

Separation on Solid Adsorbents

Silica gel was described as early as 1942 [170] for the separation of individual hydrocarbons, and activated charcoal in 1947 [171], both applications being before the development of gas chromatography as an independent technique. When first used for chromatography, very unsymmetrical peak responses were obtained with both these materials, but some improvement was obtained by adding a small amount, usually about 1·5%, of a liquid such as squalane to the solid adsorbent. This addition, described by Eggertsen *et al.* [172] gave not only sharper, more symmetrical peaks, but also reduced retention times. These two adsorbents, silica gel and activated charcoal, are still extensively used for the separation of hydrocarbons with carbon numbers 1–3, particularly where the separation and subsequent determination of any inorganic gases present is also required.

For the separation of the hydrocarbons in the range C_1 to C_5, columns packed with activated alumina to which a small quantity of some modifying liquid material has been added, are more frequently used. If alumina material as supplied by the chemical supply houses is activated and used without a modifying liquid, the peaks obtained are broad and trail as badly as with silica gel and charcoal. The modification of this material was investigated independently by Scott [23] and Hewett [24], whose work has already been described (p. 27). One column prepared from alumina and liquid paraffin as described by Hewett, has been in use in the authors' laboratory for a period of many years, and shows no sign of deterioration. A chromatogram obtained using this column for the analysis of a residual gas is shown in Fig. 61. Although all possible hydrocarbons in the range C_1 to C_4 are not present in this particular mixture, all can be resolved on this column with the single exception of isobutane and but-*trans*-2-ene, which appear as a composite peak.

This separation of the C_1 to C_4 hydrocarbons takes approximately 48 min at room temperature. For the separation to include also the C_5 hydrocarbons, the temperature is usually raised to 50°.

McTaggart *et al.* [173] achieved a separation of a mixture of paraffins and olefins up to C_4 and also of iso- and n-pentane and 1:3-butadiene—a total of 14 hydrocarbons—in less than 11 min. A 40 ft length of 0·12 in. i.d. glass tubing was used, packed with water–modified alumina and operated at 80°. The retention times of the hydrocarbons are set out in Example 9 at the end of this chapter.

Jacobs [174], using a 150 ft, 0·1 in. i.d. capillary coated with DC 200 silicone, temperature programmed from —55° to 140° at 10°/min and with 4 ml/min of helium as carrier gas, obtained a separation of hydrocarbons in automobile

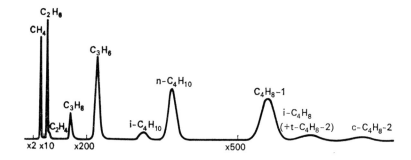

FIG. 61. Chromatogram of the hydrocarbon fraction of a residual gas. Column: modified alumina; detector: flame ionization; temperature: 25°; carrier gas: hydrogen/nitrogen mixture.

(vehicle) exhaust in the range C_1–C_{10} in 11 min, and an almost complete separation of the fourteen C_1–C_4 hydrocarbons in less than 3 min.

With the exception of methane, all the straight-chain paraffin hydrocarbon gases are absorbed on columns packed with molecular sieve material when operated at room temperatures. Branched-chain hydrocarbons are eluted from such columns. This unusual separation is difficult to achieve by any other means. At higher temperatures the straight-chain hydrocarbons are evolved and can be determined in the usual way. Such a separation has been reported by Horton [160], who eluted hydrogen, oxygen, nitrogen, methane and carbon monoxide at room temperature from a column packed with molecular sieve No. 5A, and recovered ethane, ethylene, propane, acetylene and butane by temperature programming to 300°.

Chromosorb has been used for the separation of hydrocarbons, and a chromatogram of C_1–C_5 hydrocarbons in natural gas due to Dave [175] is shown in Fig. 62.

In addition to the use of capillary columns for the rapid analysis of hydrocarbons, some experimenters have used these highly efficient systems to effect a separation of deuterated or tritiated compounds. Bruner and Cartoni [176] obtained a separation of CH_4 (180 min), CH_3D (188 min), CH_2D_2 (192 min), CHD_3 (195 min) and

CD$_4$ (198 min) using a 35 m, 0·3 mm i.d. glass column etched with 20% sodium hydroxide for 6 hr at 100°. The separation was made at −188° with nitrogen as carrier gas.

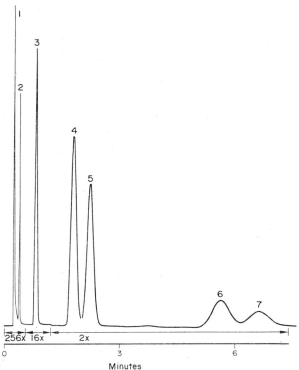

FIG. 62. Separation of hydrocarbon gases on Chromosorb 102 (Dave, *J. Chrom. Sci.* **7**, 397 (1969)). Carrier gas: helium, 58 ml/min; detector: flame ionization; temperature: 100°; sample size 50 μl.

Separation on Partition Columns

Both gas–solid and gas–liquid or partition chromatography have been used extensively for the separation of the hydrocarbon gases. A large number of liquid phases have been reported for this separation, and the choice of solid adsorbent or liquid phase will depend very largely upon the nature of the hydrocarbon mixture, and the particular separation required. Thus, when a non-polar or almost non-polar liquid is used, the separation obtained is virtually in the order of the boiling points. Such a separation may be ideal for a resolution of mixtures of the saturated paraffins, but not for example that of isobutane b.p. −6·9°, from but-1-ene b.p. −6·3° (Van de Craats [57]).

When polar liquids are used as the separating medium, the more volatile olefins are retained on the column packing longer than the corresponding alkanes, due to the greater solubility of unsaturated compounds in polar liquids. Thus, for example, when dimethylsulpholane is used as stationary phase, propane b.p. −42·1° is eluted before propane b.p. −47·7°, and the C$_4$ hydrocarbons are eluted in the order isobutane, n-butane, but-1-ene plus isobutane, but-*trans*-2-ene, but-*cis*-2-ene and butadiene. To separate isobutane and but-1-ene columns at least 15 m in length are required [177].

A more positive identification of the components of unknown hydrocarbon gas mixtures can often be obtained by chromatographing the mixture of gases on to both polar and non-polar columns. The separation obtained using a polar column can sometimes be advantageously combined with that obtained from a non-polar column, by using a series arrangement of the two columns, as, for example, described by Fredericks and Brooks [177] who used di-isodecylphthalate and dimethylsulpholane as the liquid phases. Other combinations of liquid phases using two columns in series have also been described.

A good separation of the saturated paraffin hydrocarbons from the olefins can be obtained using $\beta\beta$-oxydipropionitrile, or silver nitrate dissolved in a suitable

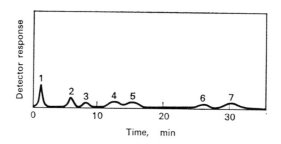

FIG. 63. Separation of unsaturated hydrocarbons using ethylene glycol with silver nitrate as the stationary phase (Bua, Manaresi and Motta, *Analyt. Chem.* **31**, 1910 (1959)). 1, paraffins; 2, propadiene; 3, but-*trans*-2-ene; 4, propene; 5, isobutene; 6, but-*cis*-2-ene; 7, but-1-ene.

glycol as reported by Bradford [36]. Using this solution as the separating medium, the paraffin hydrocarbons are eluted in a composite peak prior to the separation and elution of the olefins. The C_4 olefins are eluted in the order but-*trans*-2-ene, but-*cis*-2-ene, but-1-ene and but-1:3-diene. A separation using silver nitrate dissolved in ethylene glycol is shown in Fig. 63 [37]. As glycols are very hygroscopic, the carrier gas and the samples themselves must be perfectly dry in order to keep the separating ability of the column intact. For this reason Van de Craats [57] prefers to use a solution of silver nitrate in benzyl cyanide rather than in glycol.

Using a partition column 160 ft in length, 0·138 in. i.d., packed with silver nitrate and ethylene glycol on Chromosorb P, Lee and Rowland [178] obtained a separation of $CH_2{=}CH_2$ from $CH_2{=}CHT$, and also of $CH_2T{-}CH{=}CH_2$ from $CH_3{-}CT{=}CH_2$, but did not resolve $CH_3{-}CH{=}CHT$ from $CH_3{-}CT{=}CH_2$ under the operating conditions (0°, helium carrier gas at 0·46 ml/sec).

A wide variety of other liquids have been used as stationary phase for hydrocarbon separation, including dimethylsulphoxide and sulpholane, both of which retain unsaturated olefins and acetylenes longer than does dimethylsulpholane; heterocyclic bases such as quinoline and isoquinoline that are used to separate straight-chain from branched-chain saturated hydrocarbons; dimethylformamide that can be used only at low temperatures (0°), but gives a complete resolution of all the C_4 hydrocarbons; and γ-butyrolactone and adiponitrile.

Propylene carbonate, mixed with glutaronitrile was found by McKenna and Idleman [179] also to give a complete separation of the C_4 hydrocarbons, although some of the C_5 compounds partly overlapped the C_4 chromatographic peaks. By combining gas–liquid with gas–solid chromatography in the form of propylene carbonate adsorbed on to alumina a column can be prepared to resolve almost all the C_4 and C_5 hydrocarbons. The separation described by McKenna and Idleman using this column material is shown in Fig. 64 [180].

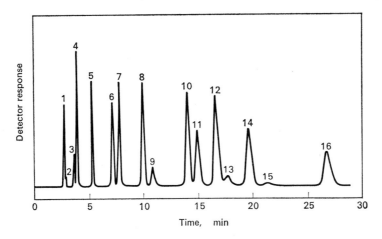

FIG. 64. Separation of hydrocarbon gases using alumina modified with propylene carbonate (McKenna and Idleman, *Analyt. Chem.* **32,** 1299 (1960)). 1, air; 2, methane; 3, ethane; 4, ethylene; 5, propane; 6, propene; 7, isobutane; 8, n-butane; 9, neopentane; 10, but-1-ene; 11, isobutene; 12, but-*trans*-2-ene; 13, isopentane; 14, but-*cis*-2-ene; 15, n-pentane; 16, 1:3-butadiene.

Acetylene is readily separated from other hydrocarbons on almost all gas–liquid chromatographic columns. A separation of methylacetylene, vinylacetylene and diacetylene was described by Kontorovitch *et al.* [181] using columns packed with dibutylphthalate on firebrick. The presence of C_4 and C_5 saturated and olefinic hydrocarbons would probably interfere with this separation. A more comprehensive separation of alkanes, olefins and acetylenes was made by Vigdergauz *et al.* [182] using a system of two columns with column switching. The first column was packed with di-isobutylphthalate on firebrick, the second with 30% sulpholane also on firebrick.

Acetylene and acetylenic hydrocarbons, particularly diacetylene C_4H_2, tend to polymerize and to form explosive acetylides with certain metals. For this reason the use of copper or brass in the construction of the column or other part of the gas flow system should be avoided as far as possible.

Open tubular columns, known more familiarly as capillary columns, have also been used for the separation of the hydrocarbon gases, largely to obtain more rapid analyses, although a more efficient separation is also obtained with such columns. Scott and Cumming [42] have described the use of capillary columns for the separation of hydrocarbons with carbon numbers of 4 and above, and Averill and Ettre [183] for the lower hydrocarbons.

A gas–solid capillary column in the form of an oxide-coated aluminium tube of 0·02–0·025 in. internal diameter has also been used [184] for the separation of the gaseous hydrocarbons. Although not necessary for this particular application, columns prepared in this way can be operated at elevated temperatures.

Detection of the Hydrocarbon Gases

Most of the earlier methods described for the chromatographic determination of the hydrocarbon gases used thermal conductivity cells as the detectors. Apart from being of only average sensitivity, such cells have the disadvantage of responding also to the inorganic constituents of the gas samples. This is of small importance where only the compounds methane, ethane and ethylene are present, as an adequate separation from the inorganic gases is readily obtained using a short column packed with activated charcoal or silica gel. However, where the C_3 and C_4 hydrocarbons are determined using a separation based on a partition or modified alumina column, then the presence of inorganic gases in the sample may interfere with the determination of methane and the C_2 hydrocarbons.

For this reason, detectors that do not respond appreciably to the inorganic gases are in general use for the determination of the hydrocarbon gases. Where these compounds are present in quantity, Scott's flame thermocouple detector is probably the most appropriate one to use. At lower hydrocarbon concentrations the flame ionization detector can be used. This detector is particularly sensitive to these gases, is simple to use and stable in operation. It has been used extensively for the determination of the hydrocarbon compounds present in such diverse materials as engine exhaust gases, flue gas, sewer gas, refinery waste gases and fuel gases of all kinds.

Another detector that has been used for the analysis of gaseous hydrocarbons is the gas burette, or Janak detector, with carbon dioxide as the carrrier gas. The volume of the accumulated effluent from the chromatographic column is recorded after absorption of the carrier gas in aqueous potassium hydroxide solution (see page 38).

EXAMPLE 1

Column dimensions	length 10 ft, internal diameter 0·1875 in.
Packing	alumina, 100–120 mesh, with 4% by weight of liquid paraffin
Temperature	room temperature
Carrier gas	hydrogen–nitrogen mixture, 75–25%, 15 ml/min
Detector	flame ionization
Recorder	1 mV f.s.d.
Sample size	1 ml of inorganic gases containing 2% of total hydrocarbon gases
Retention times	methane 1·0 min
	ethane 2·0 min
	ethylene 2·8 min
	propane 5·0 min

propene	9·0 min
isobutane	16·0 min
n-butane	20·0 min
but-1-ene	33·0 min
isobutene + but-*trans*-2-ene	40·0 min
but-*cis*-2-ene	47·0 min

Reference   Warren Spring Laboratory [133]

EXAMPLE 2

Column dimensions	length 10 ft, internal diameter 4 mm
Packing	alumina, 100–150 mesh, with 2% w/w silicone oil, and water
Temperature	17°
Carrier gas	hydrogen, 16 ml/min
Detector	flame thermocouple

Retention times		
	methane	3·0 min
	ethane	4·0 min
	ethylene	4·5 min
	propane	7·5 min
	acetylene	8·5 min
	propene	10·5 min
	isobutane	15·0 min
	n-butane	17·0 min
	but-1-ene	25·0 min
	isobutene + but-*trans*-2-ene	27·5 min
	but-*cis*-2-ene	30·0 min
	butadiene	33·0 min

Reference   Scott [23]

EXAMPLE 3

Column dimensions	length 50 ft, internal diameter 0·02 in.
Packing	alumina, 0·0002 in. film
Temperature	100°
Carrier gas	carbon dioxide, 2 ml/min
Detector	flame ionization
Sample size	5 ml natural gas followed by a 1:141 sample split

Retention times		
	methane	2·0 min
	ethane	2·2 min
	propane	3·0 min
	isobutane	4·8 min
	n-butane	5·3 min
	neopentane	9·0 min

Reference   Petitjean and Leftault [184]

EXAMPLE 4

Column dimensions	length 6 m, diameter 6 mm
Packing	liquid paraffin, 30% on 50–80 mesh Sterchamol
Temperature	30°
Carrier gas	carbon dioxide, 3 l./hr
Detector	thermal conductivity cell
Sample size	5 ml

Retention times		
	methane	3·5 min
	acetylene	4·5 min
	ethylene	5·2 min
	ethane	6·3 min

EXAMPLE 4 (*cont.*)

| *Retention times* (*cont.*) | propene | 12·0 min |
| | propane | 13·0 min |

(with the exception of acetylene, the elution order is that of the boiling points)

Reference   Van de Craats [57]

EXAMPLE 5

Column dimensions	length 80 ft, diameter 0·1719 in.
Packing	dimethylsulpholane, 30% on 30–40 mesh brick
Temperature	20°
Carrier gas	argon, 70 lb/in²
Detector	argon ionization cell
Sample size	10 ml
Retention times	propane	7·5 min
	propene	11·0 min
	acetylene	14·5 min
Reference	Kent [185]

EXAMPLE 6

(See Example 4, Chapter 7, p. 89).

EXAMPLE 7

(See Example 6, Chapter 9, p. 108).

EXAMPLE 8

Column dimensions	length 2 m, diameter 7 mm
Packing	dibutylphthalate, 23% on insulating brick
Temperature	room temperature
Carrier gas	air, 8 l./hr
Detector	flame thermocouple
Retention times	acetylene	2·0 min
	methyl acetylene (propyne)	3·5 min
	vinyl acetylene	6·0 min
	diacetylene (butadiyne)	25·0 min
Reference	Kontorovitch *et al.* [181]

EXAMPLE 9

Column dimensions	length 40 ft, 0·12 in. i.d. glass
Packing	γ-alumina, modified with water
Temperature	80°
Carrier gas	hydrogen saturated by passage over $CuSO_4.5H_2O$ at 30°
Detector	flame ionization
Sample size	0·25 ml with 1:500 split
Retention times	methane	1·2 min
	ethane	1·5 min
	ethylene	1·7 min
	propane	2·2 min
	propene	3·0 min
	isobutane	3·8 min
	n-butane	4·2 min
	but-1-ene	6·1 min
	but-*trans*-2-ene	6·4 min
	isobutene	6·7 min

but-*cis*-2-ene	7·3 min
isopentane	8·0 min
but-1:3-diene	10·5 min
Reference	McTaggart *et al.* [173]

Other examples of the separation of hydrocarbon gases are given in the following papers:

CAROFF, J., VERNON, J., BADRE, R. and GUILLERM, R. Qualitative analysis of light hydrocarbons in cigarette smoke by gas chromatography. *J. Gas Chromatog.* (1964).

PHILIPPE, R. J., MOORE, M., HONEYCUTT, R. G. and RUTH, J. M. Some hydrocarbons of the gas phase of cigarette smoke. *Analyt. Chem.* 36, 859 (1964).

ZOCCHI, F. Gas chromatographic analysis of hydrocarbons in methane in the parts per billion range. *J. Gas Chromatog.* 6, (1968).

CHAPTER 11

Nitrogen Compounds

Nitric Oxide, Nitrogen Dioxide, Nitrous Oxide, Ammonia, Cyanogen and Hydrogen Cyanide

Nitrous oxide is a relatively inert material, and its separation from other inert gases and subsequent determination by gas chromatography does not present any particular difficulty. The remaining gases are all reactive compounds, for which particular care is required if quantitative determinations or positive identifications are to be made. Whenever reactive compounds are subjected to chromatographic analysis, care must be exercised in the selection of material of which the column container is made, in the degree of activation and the nature of the packing used, and also in the "sensitivity condition" of the packing material.

It has been observed that the sensitivity to most reactive compounds increases with successive additions of the compound, until some point is reached where reproducible results are obtained. This increase in sensitivity to a reactive compound can be accelerated by the process of "conditioning", which consists of adding a sufficiently large amount of the particular component to the column in order to reach the state where reproducible results are obtained, in a single operation. This conditioning is undertaken immediately prior to the analysis, and if the "sensitivity condition" is not maintained for any length of time, then repeated conditioning may be necessary. In extreme cases the conditioning may be necessary between each determination during the course of a series of analyses.

The necessity for this conditioning of the chromatographic column and packing is usually explained in terms of a reversible chemisorption at certain sites on the column container and more particularly on the packing material. Once these sites are blocked, the normal process of physical adsorption is apparent. The process of conditioning consists, therefore, of the blocking of these particular active sites, often only temporarily, with the absorbed gaseous material.

Nitric Oxide, NO

The determination of nitric oxide by gas chromatography is complicated by the equilibrium existing between nitric oxide and nitrogen dioxide in the presence of air or oxygen, and by the dimerization of the dioxide:

$$2NO + O_2 = 2NO_2, \text{ and } 2NO_2 \rightleftharpoons N_2O_4.$$

The most frequently used stationary phase for the chromatographic separation of nitric oxide is probably still molecular sieve No. 5A. This particular separation has been found to provide an excellent example of that type of adsorption isotherm in which the retention time (or retention volume) varies with the amount of the component added. This is shown in Figs. 65 and 66, for a separation on a column 5 ft in length, packed with molecular sieve material that had been activated in the usual way. The retention times of oxygen and nitrogen, measured using this column, were found to be 0·8 and 1·2 min respectively. The carrier gas used was argon, and the detector a conventional argon ionization cell [186].

This use of the argon ionization detector has enabled very much smaller amounts of nitric oxide to be determined, than had previously been noted using gas chromato-

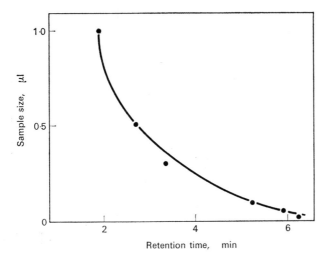

FIG. 65. Relation of retention time of nitric oxide to sample size. Column: molecular sieve No. 5A; detector: argon ionization.

graphy. For ease of handling, the very small quantities of nitric oxide that were used to obtain Figs. 65 and 66 were diluted with argon. The molecular sieve material, packed into a glass column, was operated at a temperature of 100°, and was conditioned by the addition of 170 μl of nitric oxide, added to the column before analysis. It was later found that the response, although constant for constant sample addition, attained a higher constant value if the conditioning of the column was undertaken with nitrogen dioxide, rather than with nitric oxide. No satisfactory explanation of this has yet been given.

In the presence of oxygen, some oxidation of the nitric oxide was observed to occur on the chromatographic column. This effect diminished appreciably for small aliquots of nitric oxide, and no oxidation at all could be detected with volume aliquots of nitric oxide of less than about 0·05 μl.

The tailing of nitric oxide peaks was eliminated by Dietz [187] with an elaborate pretreatment of the column packing. Molecular sieve 5A, packed in the column, was heated to 300° in vacuum for 20 hr to remove water and to activate the material, after which helium was passed through the column to minimize oxygen adsorption with a subsequent switch to a low flow rate of nitric oxide. After 1 hr the temperature of the column was lowered to 20° and the nitric oxide flow maintained for a further 0·5 hr. The column was then flushed with helium to remove excess nitric oxide. Oxygen was then introduced to convert the more tightly held nitric oxide to the dioxide. This oxygen flow was maintained at 25° for 0·5 hr and finally for 0·5 hr at 100° to complete the conversion to the dioxide. Helium was then used as carrier gas.

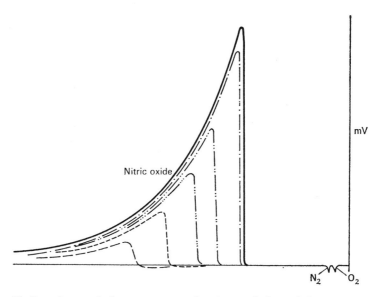

FIG. 66. Superimposed chromatograms showing variation of detector response with amount of nitric oxide. ———— 1 μl nitric oxide; ——·—— 0·8 μl nitric oxide; ——··—— 0·5 μl nitric oxide; ——···—— 0·4 μl nitric oxide; – – – – – 0·2 μl nitric oxide; — — — 0·1 μl nitric oxide.

The most striking advance in the analysis of the oxides of nitrogen, particularly for nitric oxide, has been the introduction of porous polymers such as Porapak; Fig. 67 is a chromatogram containing both nitric oxide and nitrous oxide which shows in particular a good separation of nitrous oxide from carbon dioxide. The column employed was 12 ft of Porapak Q at a temperature of 27° with a helium flow rate of 50 ml/min.

Columns packed with silica gel have also been used for the separation of nitric oxide from other inorganic gases [188], although Smith and Clark [189] reported failure in their attempts to use this material, and in similar attempts to use alumina and bentonite for this separation. Szulczewski and Higuchi [190] were, however, successful in using silica gel, and also had no difficulty in resolving nitrous oxide and carbon dioxide on a column 6 ft in length. Helium was used as the carrier gas, and the column was operated at room temperature for this latter separation, but at the temperature of a solid carbon dioxide–acetone mixture for the separation of oxygen (with argon), nitrogen, nitric oxide and carbon monoxide, which were eluted in that order.

Standard mixtures of nitric oxide in air. As the reaction of nitric oxide with oxygen to give nitrogen dioxide is kinetically of the third order, a more rapid reaction will occur at the point where pure nitric oxide is injected into large volumes of air. Once prepared, these high dilutions of nitric oxide are relatively stable. In

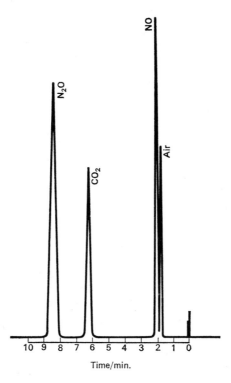

FIG. 67. Separation of oxides of nitrogen and carbon dioxide on Porapak Q. Column: 12 ft; temperature: 27°; carrier gas: helium at 50 ml/min.

order to reduce this initial oxidation Saltzman and Gilbert [191] prepared first a mixture containing 1 % of nitric oxide in nitrogen, and then prepared the standard mixtures at higher dilution from it. A similar technique was used by Kipping and Jeffery [186], employing an argon–nitric oxide mixture as the first stage of a serial dilution.

Nitrogen Dioxide, NO_2

It is generally acknowledged that nitrogen dioxide is not eluted as such from columns packed with molecular sieve material. Greene and Pust [192] have, however, shown both theoretically and practically that nitrogen dioxide, if injected on to a column packing consisting of molecular sieve material, would react with any water present in the packing, to give one-third of its volume of nitric oxide. This is then eluted and recorded as a peak identical with that obtained from the equivalent amount of added nitric oxide.

$$2NO_2 + H_2O = HNO_2 + HNO_3,$$

and

$$3HNO_2 = HNO_3 + 2NO + H_2O.$$

It has been noted by the present authors that if the molecular sieve packing material is dried for a sufficient length of time, the ability to react with nitrogen dioxide in this way is lost. The ability of such columns to separate nitric oxide is also lost on prolonged drying.

The observation by Greene and Pust [192] that one volume of nitric oxide is obtained for each three volumes of nitrogen dioxide was noted initially using millilitre quantities of this reactive gas, and was confirmed for this range by Smith and Clark [189]. Kipping and Jeffery [186] found that this ratio of one volume of nitric oxide from three of nitrogen dioxide was also obtained with less than microlitre quantities of the gaseous oxide. As with nitric oxide, an argon ionization detector was used for this work, and the molecular sieve material was carefully activated and packed into a glass column. Columns made from aluminium tubing have also been used successfully for this determination.

Morrison et al. [193] used an electron-capture detector to quantitatively determine parts per million amounts of nitrogen dioxide in nitrogen and oxygen using 0·5 ml of sample gas. Separation of the nitrogen dioxide from the other constituents, and in particular from the oxygen present, was carried out on a column packing consisting of 10% SF 96 (a methylsilicone oil) on Fluoropak 80.

The separation of nitric oxide from nitrogen dioxide was described by Bethea and Adams [194], using a 20 ft length of column packed with activated charcoal containing 2% by weight of squalane, a temperature of 22° and helium carrier gas at a rate of 66 ml/min. Nitrogen dioxide was eluted after 7 min and nitric oxide after 9 min. A thermal conductivity cell was used as detector.

Nitrous Oxide, N_2O

The solid adsorbents silica gel [188, 190], activated charcoal [189] and molecular sieve [25] have all been used for the separation of nitrous oxide from other inorganic gases. In addition a liquid phase, dimethylsulphoxide in the form of a 20:80 mixture with Silocel packed into a column 20 ft in length, is reported [195] to give a separation of oxygen, nitrous oxide and carbon dioxide in about 1 min. A separation of some inorganic gases using a 6 ft length of column packed with silica gel is shown in Fig. 68.

Smith and Clark [189] have reported that when nitrous oxide and carbon dioxide are not mixed but are introduced separately to a column packed with silica gel, then slightly differing retention times are obtained, but that when a mixture of the two was added, a single composite peak was obtained with no hint of any resolution.

Jeffery and Kipping observed a partial resolution of nitrous oxide from carbon dioxide using a 6 ft length of column packed with silica gel, and for this reason preferred to use columns packed with charcoal. Unlike Smith and Clark, however, Jeffery and Kipping noted that carbon dioxide was eluted before nitrous oxide.

The use of Porapak Q for the separation of nitric and nitrous oxides from each other, and particularly of nitrous oxide from carbon dioxide, is described on p. 120 and shown in Fig. 67.

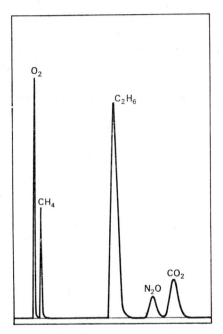

FIG. 68. Separation of some common gases on silica gel (Barber–Colman Co.). Column: 6 ft copper, ¼ in. o.d.; temperature: 28°; carrier gas: helium, 110 ml/min, 15 psi; sample size: 0·5 ml of each gas.

A thermal conductivity cell is a sufficiently sensitive detector for most purposes, and using commercially available cells little difficulty should be encountered in determining 50 ppm of nitrous oxide in air, and detecting even less. Where greater sensitivity is required, the helium ionization detector can be used.

A method has been developed by Trowell [196] for the complete separation of the three oxides of nitrogen, hydrogen, oxygen, carbon monoxide, carbon dioxide, ethane, ethylene and acetylene. The separation was accomplished using three columns in series. The first column, 1 ft in length packed with 0·5% PEG 1500 on 60–80 mesh silanized glass beads at a temperature of −76° separated nitrogen dioxide from water. The next column, 20 ft packed with 40% dimethyl sulphoxide on 60–80 mesh gas chrom RZ at 25° was essentially for the separation of nitrous oxide and carbon dioxide. The remaining column was 8 ft in length, packed with 30–60 mesh molecular sieve 13X for the resolution of oxygen, nitrogen and the remaining constituents.

Ammonia, NH_3

The trailing of chromatographic peaks noted particularly with nitric oxide is also observed to occur with ammonia. This trailing has been studied extensively by Sze *et al.* [197], with reference to the deactivation of the support material as a means of correction. Two per cent of potassium hydroxide on Chromosorb W eliminated this trailing when used with 15% Carbowax 400 or Carbowax 1540 as the liquid phase. Five per cent tetraethylenepentamine was also effective when used with Carbowax 400 or with 15% diglycerol. But for the separation of ammonia and the mono-, di- and tri-methylamines, ethylamines and n-propylamines, a 15 ft length of column packed with Chromosorb W containing 5% tetrahydroxyethylene-diamine and 15% tetraethylenepentamine was used. This column was operated at a temperature of 58°.

The separation of ammonia, methylamine, dimethylamine and ethylamine was also reported by Amell *et al.* [198], using a 6 ft length of column packed with 30% *O*-toluidine on firebrick. A thermal conductivity cell was used as the chromatographic detector.

One of the earliest separations in gas–liquid chromatography was that of James *et al.* [199], who used a mixture of hendecanol and liquid paraffin on celite, and eluted ammonia and the methylamines in the order of their boiling points. Other stationary phases used for this and for other similar separations include tri-ethanolamine by Burks *et al.* [200], a mixture of n-octadecane and n-hendecanol by Hughes [201], and a polyethylene oxide by James [202].

The first detector designed specifically for gas chromatography—the titration cell—was used by James *et al.* in these early studies of the separation of ammonia and methylamines. More recently thermal conductivity cells have been used for the detection of these compounds. Of the first four nitrogen containing gases so far dealt with in this chapter, ammonia is the least sensitive to katharometer detection when helium is used as the carrier gas. Smith and Clark [189] have reported the sensitivities of these and some other gases, and their figures are reproduced in Table 9. The poor sensitivity of a thermal conductivity cell to ammonia has also been stressed by Grune and Chueh [31]. It should be possible to effect an improvement in sensitivity to ammonia by using an argon ionization detector.

Hydrogen Cyanide and Cyanogen

The determination of hydrogen cyanide is of particular interest in the study of decomposition products, such as those of cellulose nitrate, reported by Wolfram and Arsenault [203]. The chromatographic column packed with polyethylene glycol was used to separate hydrogen cyanide from aldehydes, ketones and water also produced in the decomposition. Woolmington [204] also used polyethylene glycol as the stationary phase in the determination of hydrogen cyanide, and noted that there was some adsorption of the gas upon the chromatographic support material. This type of adsorption can now be eliminated by using suitably prepared support material.

Isbell [205] used an ester, triacetin (glyceryl triacetate) as a stationary phase for

TABLE 9. SENSITIVITY OF SOME GASES USING CHROMATOGRAPHIC SEPARATION AND KATHAROMETER DETECTION

Gas	Column	Sensitivity μg/0·01 mV peak	Retention volume ml
Oxygen	48 in molecular sieve No. 5A	0·87	96
Nitrogen	48 in molecular sieve No. 5A	1·54	212
Nitric oxide	48 in molecular sieve No. 5A	2·78	324
Nitrogen dioxide	48 in molecular sieve No. 5A (moist)	8·34	324
Carbon dioxide	36 in silica gel	13·3	340
Nitrous oxide	36 in silica gel	6·4	306
Nitrous oxide	36 in silica gel + 36 in ascarite	6·1	342
Carbon dioxide	9 in acid-washed charcoal	13·0	456
Nitrous oxide	9 in acid-washed charcoal	9·7	312
Ammonia	40 in polyethylene glycol 600 on NaOH washed but not rinsed firebrick	19·6	298

the separation of cyanogen as well as hydrogen cyanide from the permanent gases. He also showed that this material could be used to separate chlorine, cyanogen, cyanogen chloride (CHCl) and hydrogen cyanide.

The determination of hydrogen cyanide in air was described by Cropper and Kaminsky [206], who used a concentration stage in which the hydrogen cyanide gas from a 1 l. air sample was adsorbed on a silica gel pre-column unit, and subsequently released on heating. Adiponitrile was used as the stationary phase, and flame ionization used to detect the hydrogen cyanide in the column effluent.

Dinonylphthalate was used by Schneider and Freund [207] to determine small quantities of hydrogen cyanide recovered from aqueous solutions. A measured flow of air was passed through the liquid sample at a rate of about 50 ml/min, and the hydrogen cyanide in the air concentrated on a pre-column unit, also packed with dinonylphthalate dispersed on a 40–60 mesh firebrick and maintained at the temperature of a dry ice–acetone mixture. Investigation showed that the hydrogen cyanide content of the air that had passed through the solution amounted to 88% of the theoretical value, and did not change by more than 1% with changes in the gas flow rate in the range 45–55 ml/min. The gas was dried by passage through a tube containing anhydrous magnesium perchlorate included in the gas flow system in a position immediately before the pre-column concentration unit containing dinonylphthalate. The hydrogen cyanide was released by warming the pre-column unit to a temperature of 57° or thereabouts, and the gases evolved were passed to the chromatographic column, 18 ft in length, packed with 20% dinonylphthalate on Chromosorb W. The standards required were prepared by dilution of a stock potassium cyanide solution to which a phosphate buffer had been added. By using this concentration step, and by inserting an amplifier in a position between the thermal conductivity cell detector and the recorder, Schneider and Freund were able to determine concentrations of 5×10^{-4} to 10^{-6} molar hydrogen cyanide in water. They also noted that in using dinonylphthalate as the stationary phase, there was no chromatographic interference from any substance expected to be present in natural waters. Substances that would interfere if present include the methylamines, diethylamine, pentane, pentene, methanol, methyl mercaptan and high concentrations of hydrogen sulphide. Normal concentrations of hydrogen sulphide and also acetaldehyde, carbon disulphide, acetone, chloroform, ethanol and acrylonitrile are not likely to interfere.

EXAMPLE 1

Column dimensions	length 6 ft, diameter 6 mm
Packing	silica gel, 40–60 mesh, Davison grade 12
Temperature	dry ice-acetone bath for 18 min, then to 25°
Carrier gas	helium, 25 ml/min
Detector	thermal conductivity cell
Retention times	nitrogen 6·0 min
	nitric oxide 14·0 min
	carbon monoxide 16·5 min
	nitrous oxide 46·0 min
	carbon dioxide 52·0
Reference	Szulczewski and Higuchi [190]

EXAMPLE 2

Column dimensions	length 10 ft, diameter 0·25 in.
Packing	molecular sieve No. 5A, 40–80 mesh
Temperature	programmed to 400° in approximately 25 min
Carrier gas	helium
Detector	ionization
Retention times	oxygen 2·5 min
	nitrogen 5·0 min
	carbon monoxide 10·0 min
	ethane 15·0 min
	nitrous oxide 19·0 min
	carbon dioxide 22·0 min
Reference	Graven [25]

EXAMPLE 3

Column dimensions	length 24 ft, internal diameter 4 mm
Packing	silicone grease 60 parts, C-22 firebrick 24–48 mesh, 100 parts
Temperature	75°
Carrier gas	helium, 100 ml/min
Detector	thermal conductivity cell
Sample size	1·9 ml
Analysis	0·4 ml air easily separated from 1·5 ml ammonia
Reference	Grune and Chueh [31]

EXAMPLE 4

Column dimensions	length 10 ft, internal diameter 0·25 in., aluminium tubing
Packing	molecular sieve No. 5A, 20–40 mesh
Temperature	25°
Carrier gas	helium, 60 ml/min
Detector	thermal conductivity cell
Retention volumes	oxygen 180 ml
	nitrogen 330 ml
	nitric oxide 480 ml
	(nitrogen dioxide from a moist column, as for nitric oxide 480 ml)
Reference	Greene and Pust [192]

EXAMPLE 5

Column dimensions	length 20 ft, external diameter 0·25 in.
Packing	squalane, 2% w/w on activated charcoal, 65–80 (Tyler) mesh
Temperature	22°
Carrier gas	helium, 66 ml/min
Detector	thermal conductivity cell
Retention times	nitrogen dioxide 7 min
	nitric oxide 9 min
Reference	Bethea and Adams [194]

EXAMPLE 6

Column dimensions	length 20 ft, internal diameter 0·25 in.
Packing	dimethylsulphoxide, 20% w/w on Silocel, 52–60 mesh
Temperature	75°
Carrier gas	hydrogen or helium, 30 ml/min
Detector	thermal conductivity cell
Retention times	oxygen 3·3 min
	nitrous oxide 3·8 min
	carbon dioxide 4·3 min
Reference	Hill [195]

EXAMPLE 7

Column dimensions	length 3·5 m	
Packing	silica gel	
Temperature	(a) 0°, (b) −20°	
Carrier gas	helium, 30 ml/min	
Detector	thermal conductivity cell	
Retention volumes	(a)	(b)
	nitrogen 106 ml	139 ml
	nitric oxide 137 ml	195 ml
	carbon monoxide 144 ml	202 ml
	nitrous oxide 1127 ml	4525 ml
	carbon dioxide 1449 ml	5030 ml
Reference	Marvillet and Tranchant [188]	

EXAMPLE 8

Column dimensions	length 1·2 m, diameter 5 mm
Packing	polyethylene glycol 400, 40% on 30–60 mesh C-22 firebrick
Temperature	30°
Carrier gas	helium, 50 ml/min
Detector	thermal conductivity cell
Retention times	"volatile gases" 2 min
	acetaldehyde 8 min
	acetone 18 min
	acrolein 20 min
	ethyl acetate 28 min
	hydrogen cyanide 75 min
Reference	Wolfram and Arsenault [203]

EXAMPLE 9

Column dimensions	length 8 ft, internal diameter 5 mm, copper tubing
Packing	Triacetin,* 25% on 30–60 mesh Chromosorb P
Temperature	75°
Carrier gas	helium, 108 ml/min

EXAMPLE 9 (*cont.*)

Detector	thermal conductivity cell
Retention times	permanent gases 0·48 min
	carbon dioxide 0·54 min
	chlorine 0·80 min
	cyanogen 1·02 min
	cyanogen chloride 2·05 min
	hydrogen cyanide 4·35 min
Reference	Isbell [205]

* Glyceryl triacetate.

EXAMPLE 10

Column dimensions	length 18 ft, diameter 0·25 in., stainless steel tubing
Packing	dinonylphthalate, 20% on Chromosorb W
Temperature	44°
Carrier gas	helium, 135 ml/min
Detector	thermal conductivity cell (thermistor), with amplifier
Retention time	hydrogen cyanide approximately 12 min
Reference	Schneider and Freund [207]

EXAMPLE 11

Column dimensions	length 7 ft, internal diameter 0·3125 in., stainless steel tubing
Packing	polyethylene glycol 1500, 20%, on 30–60 mesh Chromosorb
Temperature	90°
Carrier gas	helium, 160 ml/min
Detector	thermal conductivity cell (thermistor)
Retention times	permanent gases 1·5 min
	hydrogen cyanide 3·5 min
	water 9·0 min
Reference	Woolmington [204]

Further references are to be found in the following:

CLAEYS, R. R. and FREUND, H. Gas chromatographic separation of hydrogen cyanide on Porapak Q. Analysis of trace aqueous solutions. *Environ. Sci. Technol.* **2,** 458 (1968).

PETROVA, M. P. and DOLGINA, A. I. Analysis of mixtures of the methylamines and ammonia by gas–liquid chromatography. *Zhur. Anal. Khim.* **19,** 239 (1964).

CHAPTER 12

Sulphur Compounds

Sulphur Dioxide, Hydrogen Sulphide and Carbonyl Sulphide

The remarks made in the previous chapter concerning the choice of materials and the condition of the chromatographic packing are directly applicable to the determination of these three sulphur-containing gases, which are highly reactive compounds. The use of copper or brass apparatus, especially for the column, is best avoided, particularly when the samples for analysis contain hydrogen sulphide. Glass columns are the ideal choice wherever possible, although polyethylene and aluminium tubing have also been used successfully. The column packing materials will require conditioning with aliquots of the pure gas before reproducible peak responses can be obtained.

Separation using Solid Adsorbents

Sulphur dioxide, hydrogen sulphide and carbonyl sulphide can be separated from other inorganic and also from organic gases using either solid adsorbents or liquid stationary phases, and little difficulty is encountered in resolving the mixtures of the three compounds. Silica gel was used by Hall [208] at a temperature of 25° to separate sulphur dioxide, hydrogen sulphide and carbonyl sulphide from each other and from air, carbon dioxide, acetylene and carbon disulphide. Hall noted that the silica gel from different suppliers varied markedly in adsorption characteristics; one supplier's product would not separate carbonyl sulphide from acetylene, while the superior adsorption characteristics of another's product provided a 100% increase in peak height. The long retention times of hydrogen sulphide, carbon disulphide and other compounds indicate that the technique of temperature programming could be used with advantage.

This difference in adsorption characteristics of silica gels was underlined during the course of an investigation by Jeffery and Kipping [16] into the use of silica gel to absorb sulphur dioxide from a gas stream. The sulphur compound was then recovered by heating the silica gel and sweeping the gases evolved on to a chromatographic column. A considerable degree of concentration can be obtained in this way, or by using activated charcoal in place of the silica gel. The activated charcoal or silica gel does not evolve any further quantity of sulphur dioxide on being heated for a second time. The capacity to absorb and concentrate the sulphur dioxide was, however, destroyed on ignition, and it could not therefore be used again.

This adsorption of gases upon silica gel has been used by Naughton *et al.* [209] for the collection of gas samples from volcanic vents at temperatures considerably above ambient. Carbon dioxide, hydrogen sulphide and sulphur dioxide were recovered in that order by slowly raising the temperature of the silica gel that had previously been thrust into the volcanic vent. In addition to overcoming this very difficult problem of sampling and collection, this procedure also avoided the further difficulty of analysing a confined gaseous sample for both hydrogen sulphide and sulphur dioxide, from which sulphur is usually deposited by the reaction

$$2H_2S + SO_2 = 3S + 2H_2O.$$

Columns packed with silica gel have also been used by Grune [30] for the separation of hydrogen sulphide and other gases. A short length of column was used, operated at room temperature. A similar separation was undertaken by Kipping *et al.* [118] (Fig. 69), using a 6 in. length of aluminium tubing, 3/16 in. internal diameter, and packed with 25–44 mesh silica gel.

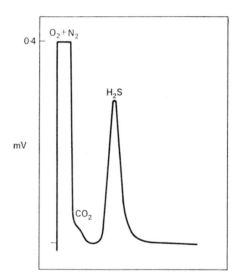

FIG. 69. Separation of hydrogen sulphide from other gases. Column: 6 in. aluminium tube, silica gel 25–44 mesh; detector: thermal conductivity cell; carrier gas: hydrogen, 25 ml/min; sample gas: air containing 1000 ppm H_2S.

The porous polymer materials have also proved beneficial in the chromatography of sulphur compounds and the chromatogram (Fig. 70) from the author's own laboratory shows the symmetrical peaks obtained with 1 m column of 100–120 mesh Porapak R operated at 75° with 12 ml/min helium as carrier gas. The porous resin Chromosorb 104, noted as useful for the separation of oxides of nitrogen and ammonia, can also be used for the separation of sulphur compounds. Examples are given at the end of this chapter.

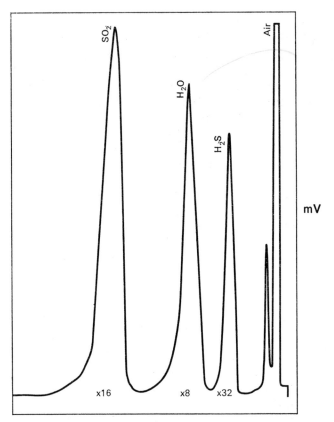

Fig. 70. Separation of some common gases on Porapak R. Column: 1 m Porapak R, 100–120 mesh; temperature 75°; detector: thermal conductivity cell;
carrier gas: helium, 12 ml/min.

Separation using Liquid Stationary Phases

Partition chromatography has also been extensively used for the separation of
the gases in mixtures containing these three sulphur compounds. Grune [30] used a
polyethylene tube packed with a silicone grease on an inert support. He recommended that the firebrick support material should be treated with aqueous sodium
hydroxide and with oleic acid to reduce the unwanted adsorption of hydrogen
sulphide on this support material. Whitson and Fourroux [210] used a silicone oil,
D.C. 500, for the separation of sulphur dioxide and hydrogen sulphide, whilst
Fox [211] used glycol to separate and determine hydrogen sulphide recovered from
aqueous solutions. Various lengths of a column packed with 28–48 mesh firebrick
support containing 35% by weight of silicone grease were used by Grune and
Chueh [31] for the separation of air, methane, carbon dioxide and hydrogen
sulphide. To improve the separation of methane from the air present, a short
column packed with activated charcoal was placed in the flow system at the exit
side of the partition column. They noted that if the charcoal was placed at the

front of the partition column, then asymmetric peaks were obtained for both carbon dioxide and hydrogen sulphide.

A 12 ft length of 30% N,N-di-n-butylacetamide on an inert support was used by Schols [212] for the separation of carbonyl sulphide from air, carbon dioxide and the hydrocarbon gases. Carbonyl sulphide is eluted before isobutane, but after propene. The presence of excess propene in the sample for analysis could give rise to difficulties in determining small quantities of the carbonyl sulphide.

Adams and Koppe [29, 213] investigated a number of stationary phases for the separation of sulphur-containing compounds. These included butylphthalate, tricresyl phosphate (used also by Ryce and Bryce [214]), and some of the Triton-X materials. These are octylphenoxyethanol compounds of the general formula

$$
\begin{array}{ccc}
& CH_3 & CH_3 \\
& | & | \\
CH_3{-}C{-}CH_2{-}C{-} & \bigcirc & {-}(O.CH_2CH_2)_xOH \\
& | & | \\
& CH_3 & CH_3
\end{array}
$$

where x varies from 1 for Triton X-15 to 30 for Triton X-305, and are available from Messrs. Rohm & Hass. Adams and Koppe were mainly interested in mercaptans, but they also included hydrogen sulphide, sulphur dioxide and water in their investigations. The solubility (and retention time) of both water and sulphur dioxide increases with increase of x, whereas those of sulphides and mercaptans decreases. A good resolution of sulphur dioxide from methyl thiol and other sulphur compounds was obtained with Triton X-305, being eluted after thiapropane (dimethylsulphide), and before thiapentane (diethylsulphide).

Bond *et al.* [215] have developed a method for the determination of both sulphur dioxide and sulphur trioxide. The mixture of sulphur oxides in oxygen was passed over oxalic acid, through a 10 ml calibrated sample loop and out to atmosphere. The sulphur trioxide is converted to the oxides of carbon and detected as such after passing through a column of phenyl cellosolve (40% w/w) on Silocel C222 to a katharometer to give a peak for the total oxides of carbon which is separated from that of sulphur dioxide. Passage of the gases through a short column packed with silica gel separates the carbon monoxide from the dioxide. Oxygen was used as carrier gas.

Detection of Gaseous Sulphur Compounds

Thermal conductivity cells have been used to determine all three of these gases with which this chapter is concerned. Using a Gow-Mac thermal conductivity cell (hot wire model), and hydrogen as the carrier gas, Kipping *et al.* [118] detected as little as 50 ppm of hydrogen sulphide in air. Schols [212], using a thermistor model of this thermal conductivity cell, reported a limit of detection of 25 ppm of carbonyl sulphide in natural gas containing 1% by volume of propene. Larger concentrations of propene reduced the sensitivity. A somewhat similar limit of detection can be expected for sulphur dioxide when a thermal conductivity cell is used.

To determine small quantities of sulphur-containing gases, Hall [208] has used an argon ionization detector. He reported as little as 3 ppm of carbonyl sulphide in a gas consisting largely of carbon dioxide, and also noted that sulphur dioxide gave a negative response with this detector.

An ingenious detection system for sulphur dioxide that could probably be coupled with chromatographic separation, was described by Bersin *et al.* [216], in which the sulphur dioxide reacts with sodium chlorite ($NaClO_2$) to produce chlorine dioxide (ClO_2). This gas then liberates radioactive krypton-85 atoms from a quinol clathrate, the radioactivity being determined using a Geiger tube. The decomposition of this clathrate has also been described for the determination of fluorine (q.v.).

The use of coulometric and reaction conductivity detectors for sulphur compounds has been discussed on pp. 52–4.

EXAMPLE 1

Column dimensions	length 12 ft, external diameter 0·25 in.
Packing	N,N-di-n-butylacetamide, 30% w/w on Kromat FB support
Temperature	28°
Carrier gas	helium, 50 ml/min
Detector	thermal conductivity cell (thermistor)
Relative retention times	air 0·115
	methane 0·128
	ethane 0·192
	carbon dioxide 0·209
	propane 0·374
	propene 0·427
	carbonyl sulphide 0·526
	isobutane 0·705
	n-butane 1·000
	butenes and higher hydrocarbons 1·000
	(using a 5 ml sample, 5 ppm COS gave a peak height of 2·5 cm)
Reference	Schols [212]

EXAMPLE 2

Column dimensions	length 4 ft, internal diameter 4 mm, glass
Packing	silica gel, 40–60 mesh
Temperature	25°
Carrier gas	argon, 200 ml/min
Detector	argon ionization
Sample size	114·3 ml
Retention times	air 1·5 min
	carbon dioxide 2·7 min
	sulphur dioxide 6·0 min
	carbonyl sulphide 16·0 min
	acetylene 23·6 min
	hydrogen sulphide 32·0 min
	(air, carbon dioxide and sulphur dioxide gave negative peaks)
Reference	Hall [208]

EXAMPLE 3

Column dimensions	length 20 ft
Packing	dinonylphthalate, 30% w/w
Temperature	90°
Carrier gas	helium, 45 ml/min
Detector	thermal conductivity cell
Retention times	oxygen 3 min
	carbon dioxide 4 min
	sulphur dioxide 8 min
Reference	Beuerman and Meloan [28]

EXAMPLE 4

Column dimensions	length 6 ft, diameter 0·25 in.
Packing	Triton X-100, 30% on Chromosorb, 30–60 mesh
Temperature	30°
Carrier gas	helium, 50 ml/min
Detector	thermal conductivity cell
Retention times	hydrogen sulphide 3·5 min
	methyl thiol 13·0 min
	sulphur dioxide 41·5 min
Reference	Adams and Koppe [213]

EXAMPLE 5

Column dimensions	length 6 in., external diameter 0·25 in., aluminium tubing
Packing	silica gel, 25–44 mesh
Temperature	ambient
Carrier gas	hydrogen, 25 ml/min
Detector	thermal conductivity cell
Retention times	air 0·5 min
	carbon dioxide 1·5 min
	hydrogen sulphide 5·0 min
	(if the sample is largely air, a complete resolution of air and carbon dioxide is not obtained)
Reference	Kipping *et al.* [118]

EXAMPLE 6

Column dimensions	2 m × 6 mm o.d. steel tubing
Packing	5% phthalic anhydride, 20% methyl silicone oil MO 1000 on 0·4–0·5 mm diaphorit
Temperature	30°
Carrier gas	hydrogen 1·2 atm inlet pressure
Sample size	2 ml
Retention times	inert gases 17 sec
	carbon dioxide 19 sec
	hydrogen sulphide 26 sec
	carbonyl sulphide 31 sec
	sulphur dioxide 37 sec
	carbon disulphide 209 sec
Reference	Brinkman [217]

EXAMPLE 7

Column	a composite column, ¼ in. o.d. comprising 20 ft 10% dibutyl sebacate on 20–80 mesh Fluoropak at 60°, 11 ft 25% potassium hydroxide on 30–60 mesh Chromosorb W at ambient temperature and 7 ft 14–30 mesh molecular sieve No. 13X at 100°

Carrier gas	helium 40 ml/min	
Detector	katharometer	
Retention times	composite peak	3 min
	carbon dioxide	3·5 min
	hydrogen sulphide	5·5 min
	hydrogen	6·5 min
	oxygen	7·5 min
	nitrogen	8·3 min
	methane	9·5 min
	carbon monoxide	11·0 min
	sulphur dioxide	14·0 min
Reference	Robbins *et al.* [218]	

EXAMPLE 8

Column dimensions	length 1·5 m by 4 mm i.d.	
Packing	80/100 mesh Chromosorb 104	
Temperature	140°	
Carrier gas	helium 50 ml/min	
Detector	thermal conductivity cell 200°, 175 mA	
Retention times	air	0·3 min
	hydrogen sulphide	0·7 min
	water	2·0 min
Reference	Johns Manville Bull. FF-189	

EXAMPLE 9

Column dimensions	length 6 ft by 2 mm i.d.
Packing	60/80 mesh Chromosorb 104
Temperature	−70° to 120° at 32°/min
Carrier gas	helium 30 ml/min
Detector	thermal conductivity cell
Retention times	SO 4 min
	SO_2 8·5 min
Reference	Johns Manville Bull. FF-189

Another paper of interest is:

GOODE, K. A. Gas chromatographic determination of sulphur compounds in North Sea natural gases by a flame-photometric detector. *J. Inst. Petroleum*, **56**, 33 (1970).

CHAPTER 13

Halogen Compounds

THIS group includes the gaseous halogens such as fluorine and the interhalogen compounds such as ClF, together with the halides of a number of non-metallic elements, and also some low-boiling alkyl halides. All these gases are reactive in some measure, and the halogens themselves together with the hydrogen halide gases are not only very reactive but also extremely corrosive. It is no longer sufficient to use glass columns and to reduce the adsorption on the packing materials–measures used for the reactive oxides of nitrogen, ammonia and the sulphur-containing gases. Each part of the gas flow system must be designed in such a way as to prevent, or at least minimize the corrosive effects of these gases. It is often desirable to construct a special gas chromatograph for the analysis of gaseous mixtures containing these corrosive gases rather than to adapt an existing apparatus. Designs for such chromatographs have been described by Ellis *et al.* [219], by Lysyj and Newton [220] and also for an in-line apparatus by Iveson and Hamlin [221]. Nickel, monel metal, PTFE and stainless steel are all possible materials for the construction of the chromatographic column, for the surface of the detector block and for other parts of the gas flow system.

Chromatographic Separation

The reactivity of the halogens and hydrogen halides limits not only the materials used to contain the flow system, but also the choice of material that can be used as the stationary phase or the inert support. Most workers in this field have used Kel-F materials, fluorinated polymer oils, available from Kellogg Corporation, or Hostaflon, a similar material available from Hoechst Chemical Company.

Despite the general belief that the materials commonly used for the separation of non-reactive compounds in general chromatographic work, cannot be used for the separation of the corrosive gases in this group, Turkel'taub *et al.* [222] have reported a successful separation of chlorine, hydrogen chloride, and other reactive chlorides, using hexadecane as the stationary phase, and celite 545 as the support material. A temperature of 28° was used, and the detector consisted of a thermal conductivity cell in the form of a brass block, with glass-coated platinum wires as the sensing elements. Dinonylphthalate was selected by Turkel'taub *et al.* for the separation and determination of chlorine, hydrogen chloride, carbonyl chloride and silicon tetrachloride, all present as impurities in boron trichloride. The separation obtained is shown in Fig. 71.

The Kel-F and Hostaflon materials can be obtained either as oils for use as stationary phases, or as a ground solid polymer for use as a support material. Ellis and Iveson [223], for example, used Kel-F 40 oil on 36–72 mesh Kel-F polymer for the separation of chlorine, hydrogen fluoride, fluorides of chlorine, and other reactive compounds. A temperature of 48° was used for the separation, argon as the carrier gas, and a gas-density balance as the detector. Lysyj and Newton [220] prepared an unusual substrate by plasticizing halogenated polymers with halogenated oils to give a "monophase gel", which they used to separate fluorine, chlorine and a number of reactive fluorides (Example 3).

The necessity of undertaking a conditioning operation when Kel-F oils are used as the stationary phase, was demonstrated by Phillips and Owens [106], who

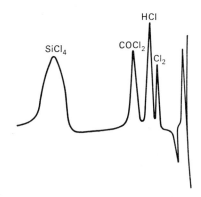

FIG. 71. Separation of some acid chlorides present as impurities in boron tri-chloride (Turkel'taub et al., Zavod. Lab. **28**, 141 (1962)).

reported that when a sample of chlorine trifluoride was introduced into a column after it had been used with hydrogen fluoride, two chromatographic peaks were produced, corresponding to chlorine and hydrogen fluoride. Similar behaviour was noted with capillary columns, which after passing eight further samples of chlorine trifluoride, gave only a very small chromatographic response for chlorine, and none at all for hydrogen fluoride. Phillips and Owens also noted that chlorine is eluted from this capillary column before hydrogen fluoride, in contrast to the elution order from packed columns operating at 60°.

Fish et al. [224] have reported the separation of the gases produced when certain chlorine containing compounds are burnt. Silica gel was used as the column packing with thermal conductivity detection to separate and detect, amongst other compounds, carbonyl chloride, hydrogen chloride and chlorine. A concentration stage was used such that 1 ppm of carbonyl chloride could be detected. Column conditions and retention times are set out in Example 10 at the end of this chapter.

Rochefort [225] passed a sample containing fluorine, UF_6, HF, oxygen, nitrogen and CF_4 first through a pre-column of sodium chloride at 60 to 70° to retain the fluorine as sodium fluoride, NaF, and displacing chlorine into the helium carrier stream and onto the chromatographic column.

Carbonyl fluoride was separated from carbon dioxide by Drennan and Matula [226]. A 6 ft stainless steel column packed with Porapak T (2 ft) and Porapak N (4 ft) was used for the separation. Helium was used as carrier and the column, which was operated at 23°, was activated by purging with helium gas for 2 hr at 200°.

Detection of Halogen Compounds

The detectors commonly used to record the presence of halogenated compounds in the eluate from the chromatographic columns include the gas-density balance, thermal conductivity cell and the electron capture ionization detector. When used with either of the preferred carrier gases, argon or nitrogen, negative peaks are obtained from hydrogen fluoride with the gas-density balance detector. As the gaseous sample components do not pass directly over the sensing elements, no special precautions are necessary for use with corrosive gases—other than those required for the whole of the gas flow systems.

In contrast, with thermal conductivity cells, the tungsten wires commonly used as the sensing elements corrode extensively, and soon burn out. Nickel and PTFE covered tungsten wires have been substituted for the bare metal wire, which leads to a prolonged useful life, but unfortunately reduces the sensitivity of the thermal conductivity cell by a factor of three or four.

As halogen atoms readily undergo the process of electron capture, compounds containing halogen atoms are particularly sensitive using detectors based upon this principle. When using an electron capture detector it is necessary to ensure that all possibility of attack by the corrosive gases upon the radioactive source is avoided, and some form of complete protection from subsequent contamination of the effluent gas by the radioactive material is necessary.

The flame ionization detector has also been used for the determination of the halogen compounds by Phillips and Owens [106]. Nitrogen or argon was used as the carrier gas, and the column eluate was injected directly into a hydrogen flame. After prolonged use, the jet showed a tendency to corrode slightly, and a "noisy" base line resulted. Chlorine, chlorine trifluoride, and hydrogen fluoride were all determined using this detector. The sensitivities were in the ratios 10:3:1, this being expected, for not only does chlorine readily ionize, but the reaction product, hydrogen chloride, ionizes more readily than the hydrogen fluoride.

Miscellaneous Methods of Detection

An indirect determination of hydrogen chloride was described by Harrison [227], in which the gas sample for analysis was passed through a 3 in. length of precolumn packed with sodium bicarbonate, placed immediately before the chromatographic column. The hydrogen chloride was absorbed by this material, liberating the equivalent amount of carbon dioxide. This was detected in the usual way, using a thermal conductivity cell after the chromatographic separation. This technique can be used for other individual acid gases, or as a means of determining total acidity.

The determination of fluorine using a krypton-85 quinol clathrate has already been noted. On exposure to certain inorganic oxidants this clathrate releases radioactive krypton atoms, subsequently detected with a Geiger tube. This detector has been used [114] to determine fluorine in air at concentrations of 1–20 ppm. Other gases that have a similar reactivity to the krypton clathrate include chlorine, bromine, chlorine dioxide, nitrogen dioxide, OF_2, NO_2F and NO_2Cl.

The well-known Beilstein test for chlorine in organic compounds has been used as the basis of a method for determining halogenated hydrocarbons by Monkman and Dubois [228]. The effluent from the chromatographic column, after passage through a thermal conductivity cell, is fed to a flame photometer having a copper element in the burner. The output from the flame photometer is passed to a second potentiometric recorder. A comparison of the two recorder charts indicates which of the original peak components contained halogen atoms. In the examples described the halogen atom was in each case chlorine, but positive flame responses would also be obtained from bromine and iodine compounds.

Coulson [79] has shown the possibility of detecting halogen compounds by microcoulometry although in fact most of his examples were not in the field of gas analysis and are therefore outside the scope of this work.

Organic Halogen Compounds

These compounds are not as corrosive as some of those that have just been considered, and conventional stationary phases can be used with celite or firebrick support materials. The conventional form of the electron capture detector can also be used following the chromatographic separation. The chlorofluoromethanes are, however, soluble in the Apiezon and silicone high vacuum greases in common use, and a specially prepared grease has been recommended [229] for stopcock lubrications when these compounds are present. This grease contains mannitol, dextrin and glucose, mixed in the proportions 7:14:36.

The separation of a number of halogen-substituted methanes was described by Pollard and Hardy [230] using gas–solid chromatography. A 30 cm length of column was used, packed with an activated charcoal. Other columns used by Pollard and Hardy were packed with dibutylphthalate, dinonylphthalate and a silicone oil, all on celite 545 as the inert support. The retention data for these substituted methanes on these four chromatographic columns are given in Table 10.

These corrected retention volumes are per gram of the separating media.

Dibutylphthalate has also been used to separate the various chloromethanes by Green [231] and by Gol'dinov et al. [232] with celite and diatomite as the inert support materials respectively. Although not strictly used for gaseous compounds, Halasz and Horvath [233] have described the deposition of carbon black in the form of a thin layer on the inside of a carefully cleaned copper capillary tube as a solid adsorbent for the separation of low-boiling chloro- and fluoro-compounds.

Greene and Wachi [234] found Kel-F oils to be not entirely satisfactory as stationary phases for the separation of fluorocarbons, and preferred to use

TABLE 10. RETENTION VOLUMES OF SOME SUBSTITUTED METHANES

B.p.	Compound	Corrected retention volumes, ml			
		4·0 g dibutyl phthalate 20°	1·89 g dinonyl phthalate 24·5°	2·14 g silicone oil 702 40·1°	1·83 g charcoal 207 B 137°
−82·2	CF₃H	2·5	1·8	0·45	7·6
−80	CF₃Cl	0·6	0·6	0·54	17·3
−40·8	CF₂ClH	21·6	17·3	5·57	53·0
−28	CF₂Cl₂	8·3	9·5	6·10	152
8·9	CFCl₂H	88·0	131·5	41·0	453
24·1	CFCl₃	171	80·5	47·0	1160
−23·7	CH₃Cl	—	27·3	22·0	57·5

$CH_2=CH.CO_2.CH_2-(CF_2CF_2)_3.H$. This material was not named, but was made available by courtesy of E. I. Du Pont de Nemours & Co. A chromatogram of some low-boiling fluorocarbons is shown in Fig. 72. CF_4 was not separated from the air present in the sample, and cyclo-C_3F_6 and n-C_3F_6 were not resolved. The peaks labelled C_2F_2 and C_4F_8-1 were only tentatively assigned to these particular compounds.

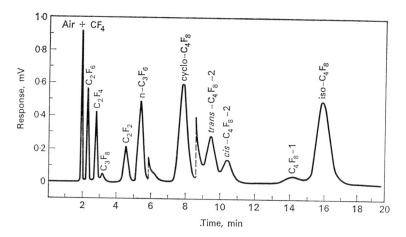

FIG. 72. Separation of some fluorocarbons by gas–liquid chromatography (Greene and Wachi, *Analyt. Chem.* **35**, 928 (1963)).

A somewhat similar separation was obtained using Davison silica gel [234] (Fig. 73). In this case CF_4 and the air peak were resolved, as also were the peaks for cyclo-C_3F_6 and n-C_3F_6. The *cis*- and *trans*-isomers of C_4F_8-2 were, however, eluted together.

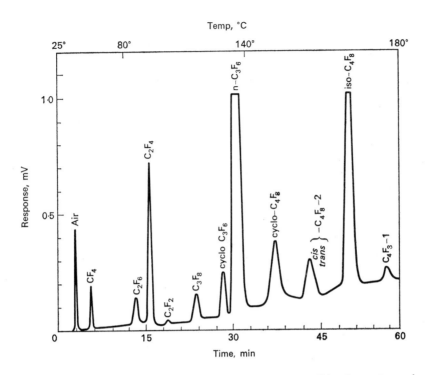

FIG. 73. Separation of some fluorocarbons by gas–solid chromatography (Greene and Wachi, *Analyt. Chem.* **35**, 928 (1963)).

EXAMPLE 1

Column dimensions	length 4 ft 6 in., diameter 0·25 in., monel metal
Packing	Kel-F 40 on Kel-F polymer, 36–72 mesh, 1:5 w/w
Temperature	48°
Carrier gas	argon, 16·5 ml/min
Detector	gas-density balance
Retention times	nitrogen 1·20 min
	chlorine monofluoride 1·40 min
	hydrogen fluoride 1·70 min
	chlorine 2·00 min
	chlorine trifluoride 2·80 min
	bromine 4·55 min
	bromine pentafluoride 6·10 min
	uranium hexafluoride 10·50 min
Reference	Ellis and Iveson [223]

Retention data are included for bromine and bromine pentafluoride, but since these two substances react with chlorine fluorides, it is unlikely that they would occur in the same gas sample.

A negative peak is obtained for hydrogen fluoride, as its molecular weight is lower than that of the carrier gas.

EXAMPLE 2

Column dimensions	length 10 ft, diameter 0·25 in., stainless steel tubing
Packing	halocarbon oil, 30% on Chromosorb W, 80–100 mesh
Temperature	26°
Carrier gas	helium, 33 ml/min
Detector	thermal conductivity cell
Retention times	silicon tetrafluoride	2·8 min
	carbon tetrafluoride	2·9 min
	nitrogen trifluoride	2·9 min
	trifluorochloromethane	3·3 min
	trifluorobromomethane	3·8 min
	sulphur hexafluoride	4·3 min
	chlorine	5·5 min
	difluorodichloromethane	5·8 min
	trifluorochloroethylene	6·3 min
	dichlorofluoromethane	12·2 min
	difluorodibromomethane	19·7 min
Reference	Lysyj and Newton [220]

EXAMPLE 3

Column dimensions, temperature, etc., as for Example 2 above	
Packing	halocarbon oil, 50%, plasticized with Kel-F powder,* packed into monel metal column
Retention times	silicon tetrafluoride	2·8 min
	carbon tetrafluoride	4·5 min
	nitrogen trifluoride	4·6 min
	hydrogen fluoride	7·0 min
	sulphur hexafluoride	12·5 min
	trifluorochloromethane	14·0 min
	fluorine	15·5 min
	trifluorobromomethane	31·5 min
	chlorine trifluoride	46·5 min
	chlorine	50·0 min
	difluorodichloromethane	56·0 min
	trifluorochloroethylene	67·5 min
	difluorodibromomethane	430·0 min
	fluorodichloromethane	448·0 min
Reference	Lysyj and Newton [220]

* Dissolve halocarbon oil 31–21 in a suspension of trichloroethylene and Kel-F moulding powder 300, 30–50 mesh. Reflux for 15 min, evaporate solvent in air.

EXAMPLE 4

Column dimensions	length 70 cm, diameter 4 mm
Packing	silica gel, 80–100 mesh
Carrier gas	nitrogen
Detector	electron capture, 24 V anode potential
Retention times	oxygen	0·5 min
	sulphur hexafluoride	1·2 min
	difluorodichloromethane	4·5 min
Reference	Gregory [235]

The detection limit is better than 2×10^{-9}g SF_6. At an applied potential of 42 V, only SF_6 is detected.

EXAMPLE 5

Column dimensions	length 320 cm, diameter 0·7 cm
Packing	dibutylphthalate, 20% w/w on diatomite
Temperature	18°
Carrier gas	nitrogen, 40 ml /min
Detector	100 cm interferometer cell
Retention times	Freon 23 (CHF_3) 5 min
	Freon 12 (CCl_2F_2) 8 min
	Freon 22 ($CHClF_2$) 12 min
	Freon 21 ($CHCl_2F$) 30 min
Reference	Gol'dinov *et al.* [232]

EXAMPLE 5

Column dimensions	length 90 cm, diameter 4 mm. Effective length reduced to 45 cm after 3 min
Packing	dibutylphthalate on celite 545 (1:2:2 by wt)
Temperature	24°, increased to 42° after 3 min
Carrier gas	nitrogen, 20 ml/min
Detector	thermal conductivity cell
Sample volume	2·6 ml
Retention times	trifluorochloromethane 2 min
	difluorodichloromethane 3 min
	fluorotrichloromethane 5 min
	carbon tetrachloride 25 min
Reference	Green [231]

EXAMPLE 7

Column dimensions	length 3 m, diameter 3·5 mm
Packing	hexadecane, on celite 545
Temperature	28·5°
Carrier gas	nitrogen, 40 ml/min
Detector	thermal conductivity cell with glass-coated platinum wires contained in a brass block
Relative retention times	hydrogen chloride 0·51
	chlorine 1·00
	phosgene 1·70
	boron trichloride 1·98
	silicon tetrachloride 7·70
Reference	Turkel'taub *et al.* [222]

EXAMPLE 8

Column dimensions	length 20 ft, 0·25 in o.d. copper tubing
Packing	$CH_2{=}CH \cdot CO_2 \cdot CH_2{-}(CF_2CF_2)_3H$, 30% w/w on chromosorb W
Temperature	0°
Carrier gas	helium, 95 ml/min at room temperature
Detector	thermal conductivity cell (hot wire)
Retention times	air 2·0 min
	CF_4 2·0 min
	C_2F_6 2·4 min
	C_2F_4 2·8 min
	C_3F_8 3·2 min
	C_2F_2 4·7 min
	$n\text{-}C_3F_6$ 5·6 min

EXAMPLE 8 (*cont.*)

Retention times (*cont.*)		
	cyclo-C_4F_8	8·0 min
	trans-C_4F_8-2	9·6 min
	cis-C_4F_8-2	10·5 min
	C_4F_8-1	14·2 min
	iso-C_4F_8	16·0 min
	(see Fig. 72)	
Reference	Greene and Wachi [234]	

EXAMPLE 9

Column dimensions	length 10 ft, 0·25 in. o.d. copper tubing	
Packing	silica gel, 50–80 mesh, Davison	
Temperature	programmed from room temperature to 180° in 60 min	
Carrier gas	helium	
Detector	thermal conductivity cell	
Retention times	air	3·0 min
	CF_4	5·9 min
	C_2F_6	13·0 min
	C_2F_4	16·0 min
	C_2F_2	19·0 min
	C_3F_8	23·0 min
	cyclo-C_3F_6	28·4 min
	n-C_3F_6	31·0 min
	cyclo-C_4F_8	37·0 min
	cis/trans-C_4F_8-2	43·0 min
	iso-C_4F_8	50·0 min
	C_4F_8-1	57·0 min
	(see Fig. 73)	
Reference	Greene and Wachi [234]	

EXAMPLE 10

Column dimensions	6 ft × 0·25 in.	
Packing	Davison 12 grade silica gel 28–60 mesh, dried 100° for 1 hr	
Temperature	56·5°	
Carrier gas	nitrogen 30 ml/min. I.P. 770 mm, O.P. 320 mm	
Detector	thermal conductivity cell 62°, 120 mA	
Retention times	hydrogen	1·0 min
	carbon monoxide	2·5 min
	methane	2·9 min
	ethane	7·0 min
	carbonyl chloride	9·9 min
	carbon dioxide	11·1 min
	ethylene	12·1 min
	hydrogen chloride	13·3 min
	chlorine	28·5 min
	acetylene	31·6 min
Reference	Fish *et al.* [224]	

Other references are as follows:

ENGELBRECHT, A., NACHBAUR, E. and MAYER, E. Gas chromatographic analysis of mixtures of inorganic fluorides. *J. Chromatog.* **15**, 228 (1964).

FORIS, A. and LEHMAN, J. G. Gas chromatographic separation of halocarbons on Porapak Q porous polymer beads. *Sepn. Sci.* **4**, 225 (1969).

GUTSCHE, B. and HERRMANN, R. Combination of gas chromatography and flame photometry for the detection of chlorine in organic compounds. *Z. Analyt. Chem.* **245,** 274 (1969).

HAMLIN, A. G., IVESON, G. and PHILLIPS, T. R. Analysis of inorganic fluorides by gas–liquid chromatography. *Analyt. Chem.* **35,** 2037 (1963).

SPEARS, L. G. and HACKERMAN, N. J. Analysis of mixtures of fluorine, hydrogen fluoride, nitrogen trifluoride, *trans*-dinitrogen difluoride and dinitrogen tetrafluoride by gas chromatography. *Gas. Chromatog.* **6,** 392 (1968).

CHAPTER 14

Miscellaneous Compounds

Water

The difficulty of obtaining any gas sample free from water has been stressed by Berry [18] in his description of the helium ionization detector. It is doubtful if any gas sample, no matter how carefully dried, can be maintained entirely free of water prior to chromatographic analysis. This universal distribution of water as a component of gaseous mixtures is the justification for its inclusion in a book devoted to the analysis of gases and gaseous mixtures.

The separation of water from other constituents of such gaseous mixtures has been accomplished using a number of partitioning liquids that can conveniently be considered in two groups, the esters and the glycols. In the first group, di-(2-ethylhexyl) phthalate was used by Haskin *et al.* [236] for the analysis of azeotropes, and in the same group tricresyl phosphate was used by Takayama [237] for the determination of impurities in commercial methylacrylate. In the second group, glycerol was used by Skriven and Hoelscher [238] for the analysis of aldehydes, ketones and water, and a polyethyleneglycol by Cain and Stevens [239] for water in hydrazine. A combination of the two groups was used by Browning and Watts [240] in the form of a column packed with glycerol and 2-bis(methoxyethyl) phthalate on firebrick, preceded by a short column packed with tricresyl phosphate on celite. This combination was used for the quantitative analysis of mixtures containing water, ethyl alcohol, diethyl ether, carbon tetrachloride, acetone and chloroform.

The detection of water has been accomplished in two ways, firstly as water itself using a thermal conductivity cell, and, secondly, by conversion to some other compound such as hydrogen, methane or acetylene. This latter compound is produced by the reaction of water with calcium carbide, and can be used as the basis of a very sensitive method of detection using flame ionization. Although this method of determination appears to be quite easy to use, in practice it is not so simple. This is in part due to the time necessary for the reaction of water with calcium carbide to reach completion, and in part to the numerous side reactions that occur, liberating other compounds besides acetylene.

Hydrogen has been generated from water present in gases by reaction with LiAlH$_4$ and subsequent separation from other gases on a column of molecular sieve 5A by Yajima *et al.* [241] and by Starshov and Voevodkin [242] by reaction of the water with sodium. These methods will determine 0·1 μg of water or less.

In order to obtain measurements of the water content of samples in the parts per million range, Carlston *et al.* [243] first effected a concentration of the water by passing the moist sample through a tube, 1 ft in length, containing polyethylene glycol 200 on celite, and cooled to a temperature of 10°. This trap was shown to retain water for a period of 4 hr, with a gas flow of 100 ml/min through it. On heating the trap to 80°, the adsorbed water vapour is recovered, and can be separated from other effluent gases on a chromatographic column, 2 ft in length, and packed with polyethylene glycol 200 on celite. By this means as little as 0·2 ppm of water in a total volume of 10 l. of the original sample can be concentrated and determined.

Although firebrick and celite materials are commonly used as the inert supports, adsorption of water gives rise to chromatographic peaks that are distinctly asymmetric. Many polar substances show similar adsorption effects, which can sometimes be eliminated by replacing the firebrick, celite or other similar material with ground PTFE, as reported by Ettre and Varadi [244].

The difficulty sometimes encountered in obtaining symmetrical peaks with water in the liquid state does not seem to be as apparent when the water is present in the gaseous state, at least up to normal saturation level. However, the introduction of porous polymer type materials has certainly made it easier to obtain symmetrical peaks for this component as can be seen in the chromatogram (Fig. 70, p. 131).

EXAMPLE 1

Column dimensions	length 2 ft, diameter 0·25 in.
Packing	polyethylene glycol 200, 30%, on 20–30 mesh firebrick
Temperature	80°
Carrier gas	helium, 100 ml/min
Detector	thermal conductivity cell
Retention times	hydrogen sulphide 0·1 min
	ammonia 0·6 min
	water 11·5 min
	benzene 1·1 min
	1-hexene 0·2 min
	cyclo-hexane 0·3 min
	isoprene 0·2 min
	n-hexane 0·1 min
	methyl mercaptan 5·0 min
	n-butane 0·1 min
	(gases that had been recovered from the polyethylene glycol trap)
Reference	Carlston *et al.* [243]

EXAMPLE 2

Column dimensions	length 18 in., diameter 0·25 in., aluminium tubing
Packing	Carbowax 1500, 20%, on 30–60 mesh firebrick
Temperature	80–90°
Carrier gas	helium, 130 ml/min
Detector	thermal conductivity cell
Retention volumes	unsym-dimethyl hydrazine 429 ml
	water 1056 ml
	hydrazine 3160 ml
Reference	Cain and Stevens [239]

EXAMPLE 3

Column dimensions	length 4 ft, internal diameter 0·25 in.
Packing	glycerol, 30%, with 2-bis-(methoxyethyl) phthalate, 20% on C-22 firebrick, with 1 ft of tricresyl phosphate, 26% on celite (to increase retention time of ether)
Temperature	25°
Carrier gas	helium, 100 ml/min
Detector	thermal conductivity cell
Retention times	air 0·3 min
	diethyl ether 1·1 min
	ethyl alcohol 2·5 min
	water 8·0 min
Reference	Browning and Watts [240]

EXAMPLE 4

Column dimensions	length 2 m, external diameter 0·25 in.
Packing	di-iso-decylphthalate, 20%, on 60–80 mesh Chromosorb
Temperature	75°
Carrier gas	helium, 40 ml/min
Detector	thermal conductivity cell
Retention times	"light gases" 1·0 min
	acetaldehyde 2·5 min
	water 4·0 min
Reference	Ettre and Varadi [244]

EXAMPLE 5

Column dimensions	length 2 m, external diameter 0·25 in.
Packing	Carbowax 1500, 10% on <35 mesh Teflon
Temperature	110°
Carrier gas	helium, 40 ml/min
Detector	thermal conductivity cell
Retention times	"light gases" 2·0 min
	acetaldehyde 4·0 min
	methyl acetate 5·5 min
	ethanol 9·0 min
	water 15·0 min
Reference	Ettre and Varadi [244]

EXAMPLE 6

Column dimensions	length 7 ft, internal diameter 0·3125 in., stainless steel
Packing	polyethylene glycol 1500, 20%, on 30–60 mesh Chromosorb
Temperature	90°
Carrier gas	helium, 160 ml/min
Detector	thermal conductivity cell (thermistor)
Retention times	permanent gases 1·5 min
	hydrogen cyanide 3·5 min
	water 9·0 min
Reference	Woolmington [204]

Silanes, Boranes and Germanes

This group of compounds, including not only the silanes, boranes and germanes themselves, but also their alkyl and halide derivatives, behave chromatographically in an analogous manner to the alkanes, with their alkyl and halide derivatives. Borer and Phillips [245] using a stationary phase consisting of silicone fluid 702 on a celite support, showed that a plot of the retention volume against the number of silicon or germanium atoms gave a straight line, at least up to n-Si_5H_{12}. In these experiments a thermal conductivity cell was used as the detector.

In a later paper Phillips et al. [246] noted that a green flame was obtained when the boron compounds are burnt, and that this green colour could be used as the basis of chromatographic detection, using a flame emissivity detector fitted with a suitable optical filter.

There does not appear to be any great difficulty in the chromatography of these series of compounds, quite conventional stationary phases and support materials being used. Their chemical reactivity makes handling prior to analysis rather difficult, and also necessitates rather more than usual care in ensuring that the column materials and packing are completely dry and out-gassed. Myers and Putnam [247] have made use of the reactivity of boron trichloride to dry the contents of the chromatographic column by passing several 5 ml aliquots of this gas through the apparatus before analysis.

These authors used a variety of stationary phases, shown in Examples 1–4, below, Copper columns of $\frac{1}{4}$ in. external diameter were used, with helium as the carrier gas and a thermistor model thermal conductivity cell as the detector. The presence of hydrogen in all their samples was observed with reasonable sensitivity—this being attributed by the authors to the more rapid warming of the hydrogen than of the helium carrier gas, on leaving the cold column and passing to the detector at ambient temperature. In the course of their experiments Myers and Putnam observed that if the partitioning liquid remained saturated with boron trifluoride, then it was possible to obtain a resolution of $BHCl_2$ and B_2H_5Cl at a temperature of 40°.

Kaufman et al. [248] used a paraffin as the stationary phase to separate mixtures of the boranes. They also used Octoil S, a slightly more polar liquid, to accomplish the more difficult separation of ethane from borane (Example 6). These authors also noted the decomposition of B_5H_{11} during the course of the analysis, producing B_2H_6 and B_4H_{10}. This decomposition was virtually complete only when small amounts of B_5H_{11} were present in the samples.

Seely et al. [249] used a mineral oil as the stationary phase for the separation of diborane (B_2H_6) from mixtures of the methyl boranes (Example 7), and noted that monomethyldiborane, the least stable of the methyldiboranes, was partially decomposed in the chromatographic column.

The separation of monosilane from its methyl derivatives was demonstrated by Russell [250] (Example 8), who used tetra-iso-butene as the liquid phase, dispersed on C-22 firebrick.

EXAMPLES 1–4

	1	2	3	4
Column length	33 ft	10 ft	18 ft	4 ft
Packing	silicone oil*	Teflon	Hexadecane*	Fluorolube†
Temperature	0°	−78°	40°	25°
Relative retention data				
H_2	0·46	—	—	0·95
B_2H_6	0·62	—	0·97	—
HCl	1·00	1·00	1·00	1·00

EXAMPLES 1–4 (*cont.*)

B_2H_5Cl	4·05	—	2·65	—
$BHCl_2$	—	1·81	4·70	—
BCl_3	—	4·54	6·30	2·72

Reference   Myers and Putnam [247]

* Dispersed on 60–80 mesh Chromosorb.

† Dispersed on Teflon.

In Example 3 the stationary phase contained residual boron trichloride from a previous sample.

EXAMPLE 5

Column dimensions	length 10 ft, 0·25 in. o.d., copper tubing
Packing	paraffin oil, 30%, on 60–110 or 60–80 mesh celite 545
Temperature	27°
Carrier gas	helium, 111 ml/min
Detector	thermal conductivity cell (thermistor)
Retention times	B_2H_6 2 min
	B_4H_{10} 7 min
	B_5H_9 19 min
	B_5H_{11} 26 min
Reference	Kaufman *et al.* [248]

EXAMPLE 6

Column dimensions	length 10 ft, 0·25 in. o.d., copper tubing
Packing	Octoil S, 30% on 60–100 or 60–80 mesh celite 545
Temperature	60°
Carrier gas	helium, 24 ml/min
Detector	thermal conductivity cell (thermistor)
Retention times	C_2H_6 2·8 min
	B_2H_6 3·5 min
	$(C_2H_5)_2O$ 15·0 min
Reference	Kaufman *et al.* [248]

EXAMPLE 7

Column dimensions	length 125 cm, 0·4 cm i.d.
Packing	mineral oil, 38 parts on 100 parts of 52–65 mesh firebrick
Temperature	0°
Carrier gas	helium, 2·73 ml/min
Retention times	B_2H_6 8·0 min
	$B_2H_5 \cdot CH_3$ 12·5 min
	$B \cdot (CH_3)_3$ 18·0 min
	$1,1\text{-}B_2H_4 \cdot (CH_3)_2$ 27·0 min
Reference	Seely *et al.* [249]

EXAMPLE 8

Column dimensions	length 4 m
Packing	tetra-iso-butene on C-22 firebrick
Temperature	30°
Carrier gas	helium
Relative retention data	SiH_4 0·27
	$SiH_3 \cdot CH_3$ 0·36
	$SiH_2 \cdot (CH_3)_2$ 0·59
	$SiH \cdot (CH_3)_3$ 1·0
	$Si \cdot (CH_3)_4$ 1·63
Reference	Russell [250]

PART III

CHAPTER 15

Some Complete Analyses

Coal Gas, Towns' Gas, Water Gas, Producer Gas, Blast Furnace Gas, Mine Air

With the exception of producer gas, all the above gaseous mixtures require the determination of the common inorganic gases and methane. In addition, the determination of the appreciable amounts of the higher hydrocarbons contained in coal gas and towns' gas is also often required. Whilst oxygen is not a normal constituent of these mixtures, it is rarely possible to assume that it is absent from the test sample where it may occur as a contaminant from air, introduced either at the gas sampling point, or at the gas plant. The oxygen determination is commonly used as a measure of the extent of this contamination. The presence of oxygen in mixtures that are normally oxygen-free indicates also that the nitrogen content of these samples is likely to be in error.

For the complete analysis of these mixtures, excluding the determination of the higher hydrocarbons, it is necessary to use separations on at least two chromatographic columns or to employ some measure of temperature programming. Two such methods of programming have already been described, both of which used columns packed with molecular sieve material. Graven [25] resolved hydrogen, oxygen, nitrogen, methane, carbon monoxide and carbon dioxide, in a method which is therefore particularly useful for those gaseous mixtures that do not contain significant amounts of the higher hydrocarbons. A somewhat higher temperature was employed by Horton [160], who eluted hydrogen, oxygen, nitrogen, methane and carbon monoxide at room temperature, and then recovered ethane, ethylene, propane, acetylene and butane by programming to 300°.

Separations obtained by the use of temperature programming are not entirely satisfactory for repetitive gas analysis, as the chromatographic column must be cooled, or allowed to cool to the low temperature required for the initial separations, before the next run can be started. This type of complete analysis has yet to be fully established on a quantitative basis, and will not be considered further.

Of more general application, and in widespread use are the methods of complete analysis based upon the use of at least two columns. The simplest system is that employing more than one chromatograph each of which is fitted with a column to enable a particular determination to be made. Thus in the analysis of coal gas or towns' gas, the determination of hydrogen, oxygen, nitrogen, methane and carbon monoxide can be undertaken using an apparatus to which a molecular sieve column has been fitted; carbon dioxide and perhaps also the C_2 hydrocarbons using

153

a second apparatus with a column containing silica gel or activated charcoal; and the higher hydrocarbons using a third apparatus with a column packed with a suitably modified alumina or a partitioning liquid. This approach to complete gas analysis was used by Kipping and Jeffery [251].

An alternative approach is to use a single gas chromatograph to which more than one column and detector have been fitted. The columns and detectors can be arranged in series, in parallel or in a combined series-parallel arrangement. Boreham and Marhoff [252] have described such a series arrangement of columns and detectors, which together with the alternative, multiple-apparatus approach is considered in detail below. Systems involving the use of two or more columns in parallel are not advocated, as these methods presuppose that the division of the sample between the columns is always made in the same way. Whilst this may be sufficiently true for some sample splitters, it is clearly not for many others. There would appear to be no great advantage to be gained in using a parallel arrangement of columns, if two or more samples are injected at separate sampling points.

Method I. The Use of More than One Chromatograph

This method was used by Kipping and Jeffery [251] for the complete analysis of the inlet and outlet gases from Fischer–Tropsch catalytic conversion plants. The inlet gases are essentially water gas mixtures, but with a high carbon monoxide content. The outlet gases contain appreciable quantities of hydrogen and carbon monoxide, but with increased amounts of nitrogen, and in addition carbon dioxide and gaseous hydrocarbons. Oxygen is not a normal constituent of these gases, but as noted earlier, its determination must be provided for.

The method of analysis designed for these gaseous mixtures is also directly applicable to those gaseous mixtures in this group that require the same constituents to be determined in somewhat similar concentration ranges. In addition, coal gas and towns' gas may require the determination of aromatic constituents, in particular benzene, that are not included in this scheme of analysis.

In the method described a total of three independent pieces of chromatographic apparatus are required. In the first of these hydrogen, oxygen, nitrogen, methane and carbon monoxide are separated from each other using a chromatographic column in the form of a copper or brass tube, 8 ft in length and packed with charcoal. This column is followed by a 3 ft length of similar tubing packed with molecular sieve No. 5A. From this column combination carbon monoxide is eluted before methane. A thermal conductivity cell is used as detector.

The gas flow system is of the very simplest kind. Argon is used as the carrier gas, and the flow is regulated by means of a good two-stage reducing valve at the cylinder head. In addition a needle valve is also provided, this proved useful but not essential. Between the cylinder head reducing valve and the needle valve on the apparatus itself, is a trap filled with molecular sieve No. 5A, in the form of uncrushed pellets, to ensure that the carrier gas supply is adequately dry. From the needle valve the argon passes to the reference arm of the thermal conductivity cell and thence to the sampling device—in this case by a by-pass chamber for syringe injection.

The carrier gas and sample aliquot pass to the chromatographic column and thence to the sensing arm of the thermal conductivity cell. The gas flow system is completed by a rotameter calibrated for use with argon that can, when necessary, be replaced with a soap-film meter.

The electrical circuit is also of the simplest kind. It is similar to that shown in Fig. 27, but with a few minor simplifications. As this apparatus is used only for routine gas analysis, the potentiometer used for varying the bridge current is replaced with a fixed resistor to give a pre-set value of the current, amounting to 115 mA. A stabilized mains-supply power pack is used to provide the bridge current. The bridge circuit is formed from the four filaments of the thermal conductivity cell. The potentiometric chain positioned across the recorder is replaced by a simple combination of two fixed resistors of 50 ohms and 200 ohms. These allow the recorder to be used at its full sensitivity of 3 mV or at a reduced sensitivity of 15 mV full-scale deflection. This position is necessary only when recording the hydrogen content of those gases with this component as the major constituent. A zero displacement device, known as "backing off", is also provided.

With the exception of the recorder, this apparatus is contained in a double box, used as a constant temperature enclosure. The thermostat is set to operate at a temperature of 35°, and is described in detail on p. 70.

A second apparatus, similar to that described above, but using a column 18 in. in length and packed with activated charcoal, is used for the determination of carbon dioxide. The argon carrier gas is replaced with hydrogen or helium and the bridge current, also obtained from a stabilized power pack, is set to a fixed value of 150 mA.

A third chromatograph is used to determine the hydrocarbons in the range C_1 to C_4. Hydrogen–nitrogen mixture is used as the carrier, and the sample is injected using a gas-tight syringe through a rubber septum directly into the carrier gas stream. A 10 ft length of column is used, packed with alumina suitably modified by the addition of 4% of liquid paraffin. The individual hydrocarbons, eluted in turn, are passed to a flame ionization detector. A chromatogram showing the hydrocarbons present in a residual gas, and the separation achieved on a modified alumina column, is shown in Fig. 61.

Using this method of gas analysis, the total of all the constituents determined in gaseous mixtures such as those listed, should approximate to 100%. In practice it has been found possible to obtain totals of between 98 and 102% without great difficulty, and for a good analyst to obtain between 99 and 101% almost every time. These results are then "normalized", that is corrected to a total of 100%. Neither water nor argon are determined in this scheme. Except perhaps for some gases composed largely of nitrogen derived from the air, serious error is not likely to arise from these omissions.

A somewhat similar method was employed by Hill and Sonley [253] who constructed an instrument consisting of four separate channels each comprising an injection system, column, detector (thermistor) carrier gas control, bridge current adjustment and attenuator. Channels one and two showed a common recording system and the remaining two channels were independent throughout.

Argon was used as carrier gas in channel one, which consisted of a 5 ft length of column packed with silica gel and was operated at room temperature: this was used to determine hydrogen only. Hydrogen was used as carrier gas for the remaining three channels and the columns were operated at a temperature of 50°. Channel two, 14 ft molecular sieve 13X, gave a separation of oxygen, nitrogen, carbon monoxide and methane. Channel three, 3 ft silica gel separated ethane, carbon dioxide and ethylene. Channel four, 25 ft 20 per cent bis(2-ethoxyethyl)adipate on Chromosorb W separated propane, propene and the C_4 hydrocarbons.

Method II. The Use of a Single Chromatograph

In this method only one carrier gas flow system is used, and a single aliquot of the sample material is taken for the analysis. This aliquot passes in turn through two or more columns which are separated from each other by the sensing elements of the chromatographic detectors—usually thermal conductivity cells, often with the thermistor elements.

The simplest arrangement is that of two columns and three thermistor elements positioned respectively at the end of the second column, between the two columns, and before the sample inlet device. For gaseous mixtures of the types listed, it is necessary to provide for the separation of oxygen from nitrogen, and for this reason the second of the two columns must be packed with molecular sieve. A 6 ft length of column packing should be adequate. The first column must then be packed with a material that is capable of separating the carbon dioxide and any remaining hydrocarbon gases from each other and from the permanent gases. Such a system has been described [254] using a 6 ft length of column packed with hexamethylphosphoramide together with a 7 ft length of column packed with molecular sieve No. 13X. Hydrogen, oxygen, nitrogen, methane and carbon monoxide pass rapidly through the first column, emerging together and giving a single composite peak response from the detector element between the two columns.

These gases are then separated from each other during passage through the second column, and are detected individually by the second sensing detector at the end of this column. During this separation the carbon dioxide and the hydrocarbon gases are resolved on the first column, and are recorded on elution by the first sensing detector between the columns. The lengths of the two columns are so chosen that only pure carrier gas passes over the first sensing detector whilst the components of the sample aliquot are passing over the second, and vice versa.

A more complicated system was described by Boreham and Marhoff [252] in which a total of five thermistor elements are used, the appropriate element being switched electrically into the bridge circuit at the predetermined time. Thermistors not in the bridge circuit are kept "ready" in a subsidiary heating system.

The first column is packed with silica gel, the second with molecular sieve, but each column is divided and a thermistor detector element positioned between the two parts of each column, as well as between the two columns, before the sample inlet mechanism and at the end of the second column. All the molecular sieve part of the column is activated in the usual way, but the first part of the silica gel column is deactivated by the addition of water, giving an improved resolution.

The carrier gas flow system is as follows. The carrier gas from the cylinder supply is fed via a suitable regulator to the reference thermistor bead and then to the sample introduction system. The gas now passes in turn to the first silica gel unit, a column 2 m in length, packed with 40–60 mesh material deactivated with 4% water, and thence to the first (No. 1) sensing thermistor. This is followed by the second silica gel column, similar to the first but not deactivated. This is followed by the second sensing (No. 2) thermistor, and the first molecular sieve column. This is also 2 m in length, and is packed with 40–60 mesh material suitably activated. The carrier gas then flows to the third (No. 3) sensing thermistor, the final part of the chromatographic column, similar in all respects to the previous molecular sieve unit, and finally to the last (No. 4) sensing thermistor and the outlet.

This system of Boreham and Marhoff was designed for the analysis of fuel gases, the components of which are detected in the following order. The number noted beside each constituent is that of the sensing thermistor used to record that particular component, these sensing thermistors being switched into the bridge circuit at the appropriate time and in the following order:

ethane	No. 1
carbon dioxide	No. 1
oxygen	No. 4
propane	No. 1
nitrogen	No. 4
methane	No. 3
propene	No. 1
isobutane	No. 1
carbon monoxide	No. 4
ethylene	No. 2
two butenes	No. 1

The complicated switching system that is a feature of this apparatus is a distinct disadvantage. Another disadvantage is that in order to determine carbon dioxide with any degree of accuracy, either hydrogen or helium must be used as the carrier gas. In which case the hydrogen content of the sample cannot be determined. The sensitivity to the minor constituents is also relatively poor, although it is possible to effect some improvement by increasing the sample size and making appropriate choice of carrier gas.

A simple arrangement for the determination up to and including the C_2 hydrocarbons and including water has been reported by Forsey [255] using a series arrangement of Porapak Q and molecular sieve. The latter separates the light components after they have passed through the Porapak as a composite peak. The molecular sieve is then switched out of the system as CO_2, H_2O and the C_2 hydrocarbons are eluted from the Porapak.

The chief advantage of this method lies in the need for only one gas chromatograph and recorder. This is not so much of an advantage as it would at first seem, as the two chromatographs used as the basis of Method 1, can also be built into a common constant temperature enclosure, and use the same recorder (and also the same zero suppression circuit) which can be switched from one bridge circuit to the other as required. Although not quite as versatile as two single, independent gas chromatographs, one such twin unit in the authors' laboratory has proved to be an ideal arrangement where the gas samples for analysis do not change appreciably in composition over a period of time.

Although it is possible, as in the method of Boreham and Marhoff, to select chromatographic columns for the separation of the C_2 and higher hydrocarbons at the same time as the separation of the inorganic gases, the introduction of the flame ionization detector has rendered such methods obsolete. The inherent sensitivity and selectivity of this ionization detector have made the use of an independent chromatograph well worth while, if the hydrocarbon content of many samples is required.

For fuel gases this determination is often essential, but for the simpler mixtures such as producer gas, blast furnace gases and mine air, the determination of the inorganic gases and methane is sufficient. For these mixtures a very much simplified version of the Boreham and Marhoff apparatus can be used, or a simple twin katharometer unit (or two separate units) if Method I is selected.

The analysis of mine airs using a method very similar to that described as Method 1 has been given by Vizard and Wynne [256] and also by Baker and Hartwell [257], using the recorder base-line displacement technique already described. Method I has also been used by Fells *et al.* [258] for the analysis of fuel gases, with a silica gel packing for the separation and determination of carbon dioxide, C_2 and the higher hydrocarbons. Method I can also be used for the analysis of refinery gases, although in this case, the inclusion of the third chromatograph for the determination of the individual hydrocarbons in the range C_1 to C_4 is essential.

Engine Exhaust Gases

The inorganic and hydrocarbon content of petrol exhaust gases can also be determined by Method I using a combination of gas chromatographs. In addition to the C_1 to C_4 hydrocarbons normally determined in fuel gas mixtures, such exhaust gases contain C_5 and higher hydrocarbons. For the determination of these compounds, the temperature of the chromatographic separation can be increased to 40° or even higher.

The carbon monoxide and hydrogen content of diesel engine exhaust gases are too low to be determined using the chromatographs designed for the complete analysis of fuel gas mixtures on a routine basis. The required sensitivity to carbon monoxide can be obtained by using a short length of column packed with molecular sieve as the separating medium, and either hydrogen or helium as the carrier gas. It should also be possible to determine both hydrogen and carbon monoxide in diesel exhaust gases using the helium ionization detector, and pure helium as the carrier gas.

Jeffery and Kipping [259] suggest such a scheme and also indicate possibilities for the determination of the sulphur and nitrogen oxides formed. However, better schemes for these reactive gases are now available with the advent of porous polymer type materials and reference to the earlier chapters in this volume will also indicate conditions appropriate to the determination of these compounds.

Sludge Digestion Gas

Anaerobic digestion of domestic sludge produces a number of specific gaseous products including methane, carbon dioxide, hydrogen sulphide and ammonia. The gas evolved from this process contains also oxygen and nitrogen. Carbon monoxide and hydrogen may also be produced in small amounts, although Grune [30] was unable to detect any trace of hydrogen in the gas produced from laboratory digestors.

An elegant method for determining oxygen, nitrogen, methane, and carbon dioxide in the gas from the sludge digestors, using single sample injection has been described in "Notes on some methods of gas analysis" by members of the staff of the Water Pollution Laboratory [167]. In this method the sample is injected into a stream of hydrogen as carrier gas (helium can also be used), and is dried by passage through anhydrous calcium sulphate ("Drierite") and magnesium perchlorate ("Anhydrone"), before passing to a short length of column containing silica gel. In this column the carbon dioxide present is separated from all other constituents of the sample aliquot. The eluate from the column then flows through one arm of a two-element hot-wire, thermal conductivity cell, by which the carbon dioxide is detected.

The gas stream then passes through a tube containing potassium hydroxide to remove the carbon dioxide, and then to the second column packed with molecular sieve No. 5A, in which the separation of oxygen, nitrogen and methane then takes place. These gases are then sensed in turn during the passage through the second arm of the thermal conductivity cell. The lengths of the two chromatographic columns are so arranged that when constituents of the sample are passing through one arm, the other arm contains only pure hydrogen.

Grune and Chueh [31] suggest using a number of columns for the determination of the various constituents of sludge digestion gas. A column packed with molecular sieve No. 5A is used in conjunction with a thermal conductivity cell to determine oxygen, nitrogen and methane. By using argon as the carrier gas, any hydrogen present would be recorded, and the oxygen result obtained would be "argon-free oxygen". Carbon monoxide may also be present, but in amounts too small to give detectable chromatographic peaks from this injection. If required separately, argon could be determined by using a short column packed with molecular sieve operated at a low ($-78°$) temperature. Carbon dioxide is separated using a short column packed with silica gel, or a somewhat longer column if the complete separation of air, methane and carbon dioxide is required.

The coexistence of hydrogen sulphide and ammonia in wet sludge gas is stated to be unlikely. Hydrogen sulphide can be separated from carbon dioxide and the other gases present using a 12 ft length of column packed with silicone grease on firebrick, in the ratio 60:100. This column absorbed most of the ammonia irreversibly. None of the columns used were completely satisfactory for the separation of ammonia.

CHAPTER 16

Determination of Gases
in Solid Sample Materials

GASEOUS components are not unusual constituents of solid materials. All solids contain a certain amount of gas physically adsorbed on the surface of the solid particles. Some gas may also occur in pockets or holes within the particles, or even dissolved in the solid itself. Gases can also occur in a combined form, such as carbon dioxide in limestones and carbonate minerals. Other examples of gases that may be obtained from solids, although not present as such, include carbon dioxide and sulphur dioxide from steel samples, and carbon dioxide, water, sulphur dioxide and nitrogen from organic materials, obtained following oxidation of the parent element, alloy or compound.

The chromatographic apparatus required for the determination of such gases is usually of the simplest kind, generally consisting of an appropriate column, a thermal conductivity cell and a simple bridge circuit. These topics have been considered in detail earlier in this book, and no further description is necessary here. As with the determination of gases evolved from liquid samples, which is considered in Chapter 17, the greatest difficulties are likely to arise in the operations leading to the recovery of the gaseous material.

One of the simplest ways of recovering gases from a solid is to melt the material and strip the contained gas with a stream of an inert gas. Despite the obvious practical difficulties involved in these operations, such a method is feasible and has been used by Kashima and Yamagaki [260] to determine hydrogen in aluminium metal. Nitrogen was used to strip the hydrogen from the molten aluminium and the determination was completed chromatographically. The same authors [261] have also determined hydrogen in cast iron by heating samples of the metal to a temperature of 750° in a stream of argon, and determined the hydrogen content of the argon gas at intervals. Oxygen and nitrogen have been determined in steels by fusing the sample in preheated graphite crucibles and determining the carbon monoxide formed and the nitrogen released. Koch and Lemm [262] first determined the carbon monoxide by infra-red absorption but Kashima and Yamagaka [263] analysed both gases by gas chromatography as did Bryan and Bonfiglio [264].

Winge and Fassel [265] used a d.c. carbon arc and a platinum flux to extract and determine the oxygen (as carbon monoxide) and nitrogen content of refractory metals, the gases being liberated into a static helium atmosphere, an aliquot of which was then passed to the chromatographic column.

The most popular method for the extraction of dissolved gases from metallic samples is, however, by vacuum fusion. Lewis and Melnick [266] used this technique to determine the oxygen and nitrogen content of metals—in particular of some standard steels. A Beckman model CC-1 gas chromatograph was used with a thermal conductivity detector as the sensing element, in conjunction with a column packed with molecular sieve to separate the two gases obtained. In place of the gas sampling valve used for conventional gas analysis, an adsorption loop 13 in. in length, $\frac{1}{4}$ in. external diameter made of copper tubing was fitted to the chromatograph. This loop contained 2 g of molecular sieve No. 5A pellets, held in place with glass wool, and was used as follows. Stopcock 1 in Fig. 74 was closed, stopcock 2 opened, and the adsorption loop outgassed under vacuum. Stopcock 2 was then closed and the gas sample, extracted under vacuum from the hot metal, was adsorbed on the molecular sieve pellets, now cooled with liquid nitrogen or oxygen. After closing stopcock 1, the valve was then rotated to divert the helium carrier gas through the adsorption loop at a flow rate of 70 ml/min, while the loop was heated to a temperature of 300°.

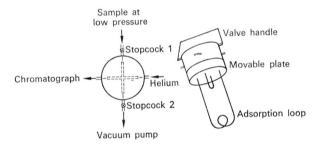

FIG. 74. Gas sampling valve for vacuum extraction (Lewis and Melnick, *Analyt. Chem.* **34**, 868 (1962)).

A 6 ft length of column packed with molecular sieve was used for the separation of the gases involved. Chromatographic peaks were obtained for hydrogen, oxygen, nitrogen and carbon monoxide, but only oxygen and nitrogen were determined.

Galwey [267] and Juranek and Ambrova [268] have described methods for the determination of carbon in ferrous materials, and Hillen and Thackray [269] have determined the concentration of helium and hydrogen in the gases extracted by vacuum melting of irradiated beryllium. Galwey used an argon gas chromatograph to measure the carbon dioxide formed on oxidation of the alloyed carbon. Negative peak responses are obtained for carbon dioxide using an argon chromatograph in this way. This, and the poor sensitivity obtained, suggest that this instrument is not ideal for this purpose. Galwey burnt the steel samples in a stream of oxygen at a temperature of 1050–1100°, and passed the gases obtained into a thin-walled double U-trap immersed in liquid nitrogen. This trap formed the by-pass loop of a sample injection system. After adsorption of the gases in the trap was complete it was carefully evacuated to remove the excess oxygen, the stopcocks at each end of the trap were closed and the contents allowed to warm to room temperature. The argon carrier gas was then diverted through the trap and to the chromatographic column.

This column was 60 cm in length, packed with activated charcoal 100–120 mesh, and maintained at a temperature of 100°. Peaks were obtained for oxygen, carbon dioxide and also, when the original material contained sulphur, for sulphur dioxide. No results were given to indicate the reliability of the sulphur measurements, but carbon was determined with an accuracy of $\pm0\cdot1$ mg in the range 0–3·0 mg total carbon, using steel samples 1–2 g in weight.

Carbonate Rocks and Minerals

The carbon dioxide content of carbonate rocks and minerals can readily be determined by first liberating the carbon dioxide with mineral acid and then subjecting the gases evolved to chromatographic separation and determination. Carpenter [270], for example, liberated the carbon dioxide with 3N hydrochloric acid in a closed system, and when the reaction was complete, extracted a known volume of the liberated gases and injected this into a conventional gas chromatograph, fitted with a thermal conductivity cell as detector, and a column packed with silica gel. The detection limit was given as 0·2 ppm (by weight).

A somewhat different approach was used by Jeffery and Kipping [15] in that the carbonate samples were decomposed with orthophosphoric acid in a reaction vessel attached to the chromatograph, so that all the carbon dioxide liberated was used for the determination. A conventional detection system was used with a thermal conductivity cell and bridge network. The column was packed with silica gel. The reaction vessel and the gas flow system are shown in Fig. 75. The round bottomed reaction vessel has a capacity of about 12 ml, and a gas-storage vessel of about 50 ml capacity is provided to hold the carbon dioxide prior to elution with the hydrogen carrier gas. A drying tube, about 4 in. long, packed with a coarse grade of silica gel, was included in the flow system to prevent the rapid deterioration of the chromatographic column. This drying tube can be regenerated when necessary by heating it *in situ*, with carrier gas passing through it and out to atmosphere. The reaction vessel is completed by a series of stopcocks permitting the hydrogen gas to pass from the reference arm of the thermal conductivity cell to the chromatographic column either directly or via the reaction vessel. The conical ground glass joints of the reaction vessel are fitted with PTFE sleeves and are heavily spring-loaded. The ball joint is also spring loaded and is carefully lubricated with Apiezon T grease.

With hydrogen gas passing directly from the reference arms of the thermal conductivity cell to the chromatographic column, the tap A is opened to the reaction vessel, followed by tap B. Both of these taps are then closed when 1–2 ml of the diluted $(1 + 1)$ phosphoric acid has flowed from the funnel into the reaction flask containing the weighed sample. The mercury reservoir is lowered to accommodate the gas from the reaction vessel in the storage vessel. The contents of the flask are boiled gently for 2–3 min with a microburner, and are then cooled by immersion in a beaker of cold water. The gas from the storage vessel is then transferred back to the reaction vessel by raising the height of the mercury reservoir. Tap C is turned to the position in which the gas from the reaction vessel passes to

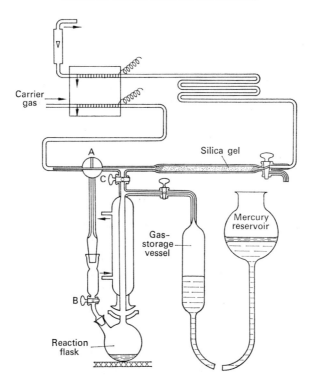

FIG. 75. Apparatus for the determination of carbon dioxide in rocks and minerals
(Jeffery and Kipping, *Analyst*, **87,** 379 (1962)).

the column, and taps *A* and *B* are opened to complete the flow of carrier gas via the
reaction flask. The apparatus is calibrated by carrying out this determination as
described, but by using a sample of pure calcium carbonate.

A later model of this apparatus has dispensed with the storage vessel and mercury
reservoir, substituting instead a means of partial evacuation of the reaction vessel.

This method of determining carbon dioxide, as described by Carpenter or by
Jeffery and Kipping, can be used for the determination of other gases that can be
liberated by a simple chemical reaction.

The Determination of Other Gases in Rocks and Minerals

The relatively complicated and expensive vacuum fusion technique can be used
for the recovery of gaseous constituents of rocks and minerals. A much simpler
method was described by Jeffery and Kipping [115] in which the samples were
heated with a suitable flux in a platinum boat. This fusion was conducted in a small
silica tube attached to a gas chromatograph, shown in Fig. 76. This tube is approximately 6 in. in length, and is connected to the gas flow system through a silica ball
joint. Two small metal plates, with holes of the appropriate size, were bolted
together across this ball joint, in place of the spring clip supplied, which did not

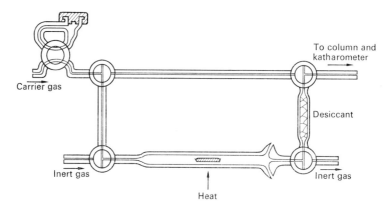

FIG. 76. Apparatus for the recovery of gases from rocks and minerals using a fusion technique (Jeffery and Kipping, *Analyst*, **88,** 266 (1963)).

keep the joint gas-tight. With these plates in position and the outer part of the ball joint lightly smeared with Apiezon T grease, a gas-tight joint was obtained. The apparatus as shown in the figure was that used by the authors, but could probably be improved by using a second ball joint at the other end of the furnace tube. This joint would also require to be made gas-tight in the same way.

The desiccant is incorporated only to prevent the rapid deterioration of the chromatographic column, which would otherwise require regeneration at intervals of about 10 days. A coarse grade of silica gel was used, but other desiccants would be equally effective.

The remainder of the apparatus, not shown in the figure, consists of the conventional thermal conductivity cell with associated bridge network, potentiometric recorder, gas-flow controls and measuring devices, all of the usual pattern.

For the separation of hydrogen, oxygen, nitrogen, and carbon monoxide a column 6 ft in length packed with molecular sieve No. 5A was used. This column was also used for the determination of helium and argon. For the separation of carbon dioxide a 2 ft length column packed with activated charcoal was used. The choice of carrier gas depended upon the constituent to be determined. An inert gas supply was also provided for use with hydrogen as the carrier gas.

For the decomposition of a 50 mg portion of ground rock material, approximately 0·15 g of a mixed sodium tetraborate glass-sodium tungstate flux [271] was weighed into a small platinum boat, and fused thoroughly to ensure the complete expulsion of all absorbed gases. After cooling rapidly in a desiccator, the 50 mg sample of ground material was weighed on to the flux, and the boat and contents transferred to the silica tube. The reactor assembly was then completed as shown in the diagram and the gas present in the reactor displaced with the carrier gas (or nitrogen if hydrogen is to be used as carrier).

With the carrier gas passing directly to the thermal conductivity cell, the tube was heated for a sufficient length of time to ensure the complete fusion of the sample and the expulsion of the gaseous constituents. After cooling, the carrier gas was diverted through the ignition tube to the detector in the usual way. The katharometer response was calibrated by introducing aliquots of the pure gases into the carrier gas stream, using a by-pass sample injector, again in the usual way.

For the determination of helium, hydrogen was used as the carrier gas, and the ignition undertaken in an atmosphere of nitrogen. No difficulty was experienced in separating the helium obtained from a number of uranium-bearing minerals from the great excess of nitrogen present (Fig. 77). Argon was used as the carrier gas for the determination of hydrogen, oxygen and nitrogen. It was also found possible to determine argon, but a very much larger sample was necessary, and as the apparatus could not be used to fuse such large samples, the gases were recovered from them by direct ignition.

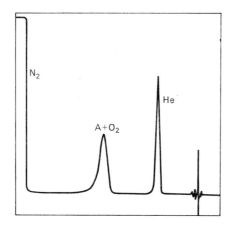

FIG. 77. Chromatogram of gases obtained from a sample of pitchblende (Jeffery and Kipping, *Analyst*, **88**, 266 (1963)). Carrier gas: hydrogen; column; molecular sieve; sample fused in an atmosphere of nitrogen.

By coupling an apparatus for the ignition of rock material with a commercial gas chromatograph fitted with flame ionization detector and a modified alumina column, it was possible to demonstrate that a large number of organic compounds were formed or liberated during ignition. Those detected include methane, ethane, ethylene, propane, propene, acetylene, isobutane, but-1-ene, iso-butene and but-2-ene.

The Analysis of Organic Compounds

The ease with which carbon compounds can be converted to carbon dioxide and water, has led to the use of gas chromatography for the determination of carbon and hydrogen in organic materials. Duswalt and Brandt [272] have described a procedure in which this oxidation to carbon dioxide and water is followed by a conversion of the water to acetylene by reaction with calcium carbide. Nitrogen present in a combined form can also be determined after conversion to gaseous nitrogen. Parsons *et al.* [273] also determined nitrogen after conversion to gaseous nitrogen, but absorbed the carbon dioxide and water formed during the oxidation.

By using a copper oxide catalyst Reitsema and Allphin [274] converted the organic nitrogen to nitrogen dioxide prior to chromatographic determination. Any sulphur present in organic material is converted to sulphur dioxide on oxidation of the carbon and hydrogen. Beuerman and Meloan [28] determined this sulphur dioxide after separation in a trap at liquid nitrogen temperature, using a column packed with dinonylphthalate.

CHAPTER 17

Determination of Gases in Liquid Sample Materials

As with the determination of gases in solid materials, the chromatographic separation of the gases liberated from liquid sample materials is often a relatively simple matter. Extensive or complicated apparatus is seldom required, and the methods used follow closely those that have already been described in the earlier chapters. Where it is necessary to undertake complete analysis of permanent gas mixtures recovered from solution, it is generally preferable to use Method II (p. 156), using two or more columns in series, rather than Method I (p. 154), which requires a greater amount of gaseous sample.

This chapter is particularly concerned with the methods that have been used for the recovery of gases from liquid materials prior to undertaking their chromatographic separation. Four general methods are in common use and, although there is some degree of overlap between them, they may conveniently be considered in the following groups:

Boiling out methods
Vacuum extraction
Stripping techniques
Direct injection of the liquid sample (to the column or precolumn unit).

What is important in recovering gases from a liquid sample is to ensure that the mixture subsequently analysed is representative of the gases present in the liquid phase, or alternatively represents a complete recovery from the liquid of the constituent of interest.

Boiling Out Methods

In these methods the gaseous constituents of interest are removed by boiling the liquid phase—either as supplied, or after the addition of a suitable reagent to liberate the required constituent. This method was used by Jeffery and Kipping [275] to determine carbon dioxide and nitrous oxide dissolved in aqueous solutions of monoethanolamine.

The basic apparatus used for this recovery has earlier been used for the determination of carbon dioxide in rock and mineral samples. It is described in detail in the previous chapter, and is shown in Fig. 75. The flask used for the sample decomposition was, however, replaced with a flask of similar size, and with the same size ball joint for connection to the remaining part of the apparatus, but with provision for removing the liquid sample from the flask, as shown in Fig. 78.

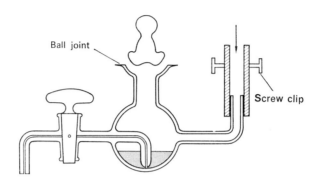

FIG. 78. Reaction vessel for the recovery of nitrous oxide from solution (Jeffery and Kipping, *Analyst*, **87**, 594 (1962)).

The evolution of the nitrous oxide was readily achieved by boiling the solution in the reaction vessel. When such boiled solutions were left in the reaction flask, small amounts of the gas redissolved on cooling. For this reason, the samples were removed from the apparatus immediately after boiling. When these samples were replaced in the flask and boiled for a second time, no further nitrous oxide could be recovered. The nitrous oxide recovered from the solution was separated from the air, and any carbon dioxide present, on a column packed with activated charcoal. Although hydrogen was used as the carrier gas, a safer choice would be to use helium. The thermal conductivity cell was calibrated by measuring the peak areas produced when known amounts of nitrous oxide were injected on to the column, either through the rubber tubing which soon needed replacement, or preferably using a by-pass sample injector inserted into the gas flow system.

The determination of dissolved carbon dioxide was made in the same way as the determination in solid samples described in the previous chapter, except that the sample aliquot was transferred to the flask by pipette instead of by direct weighing. The carbon dioxide was liberated with phosphoric acid, and there was no need to remove the sample after boiling, as carbon dioxide is not appreciably soluble in acid solutions.

It is not always necessary for the extraction apparatus to be connected to the flow system of a gas chromatograph. For example Curry *et al.* [276] determined a number of volatile poisons in blood by injecting 1 ml of the blood sample into a small cylindrical apparatus, about 7 ml in capacity, fitted with two side arms. One of these side arms was fitted with a serum cap for the injection of the liquid and for the subsequent removal of the gas sample, whilst the other, used for cleaning purposes, was closed with a ground glass stopper. The vessel contained about 0·5 g of solid potassium carbonate, and after injection of the sample, the apparatus was warmed to about 70°, by immersion in hot water for 1 min. The vapour pressure of the water in the sample is decreased by the presence of the potassium carbonate and the heat of solution of the solid provides some internal heating.

A 1 ml aliquot of the gas contained in the vessel was taken through the serum cap, and injected into a conventional gas chromatograph with a partition column, 12 ft in length, packed with 10% silicone oil on 60–80 mesh Embacel, at room temperature. Hydrogen gas was used as the carrier, and flame ionization as the detector. The following common volatile poisons were easily separated and detected—halothane, chloroform, carbon tetrachloride, ethanol, acetone, tri-chloroethylene, and paraldehyde. The determination of these substances was completed by a comparison with control samples. The particular column used did not resolve acetone and ethanol, but the two could be distinguished (assuming that both were not present), by the trailing peak exhibited by alcohol. Paraldehyde has a relatively high retention time and Curry et al. recommended that if many samples are to be examined, then the potassium carbonate should be replaced by 1 ml of dilute sulphuric acid, to give acetaldehyde which is then eluted close to ether.

A method also depending upon the heating of the sample was used by Elsey [277] for the determination of dissolved oxygen in oil. The oil sample was injected into a glass tube connected to a gas chromatograph in place of the by-pass sample injector. The serum cap is positioned midway between two fritted discs, 5 in. apart at either end of the tube, and the whole unit maintained at a temperature of 75°. When a stable base line was obtained with the helium carrier gas passing through the empty tube, the oil sample was injected through the serum cap and into the compartment isolated by the fritted discs. Oxygen and other dissolved gases were stripped from the oil, and carried by the helium to the chromatographic column. The residual oil was drained after each determination, and the stripping unit rinsed with hexane.

Vacuum Extraction

Vacuum methods possess the advantage that the extraction of the gaseous material from the solution is much more rapid than when methods based upon boiling or stripping are used. Natelson and Stellate [278] used a vacuum technique to recover oxygen and nitrogen from jet fuel and oxygen and carbon dioxide from blood, the solvent being removed to a storage chamber.

The vacuum chamber employed by Roxburgh [279] for the determination of oxygen utilization in fermentation is illustrated in Fig. 79. It is flushed with the carrier gas, in this case hydrogen, and then filled with mercury from the leveling bulb (not shown), stopcock 2 being closed. Stopcock 3 is used to vent the hydrogen from the tube and is closed when the tube is full of mercury, hydrogen carrier gas flowing in the meantime along the by-pass through stopcock 1. A sample of 5–15 ml was then injected through the serum cap and stopcock 4, with stopcock 5 open. With stopcock 4 closed, the mercury level was then readjusted to just above stopcock 5. Gentle shaking for 15–20 sec extracted substantially all the dissolved oxygen and nitrogen. The liquid level was then raised to the top of the capillary tube between the upper and lower chambers and stopcock 5 closed. The gas sample

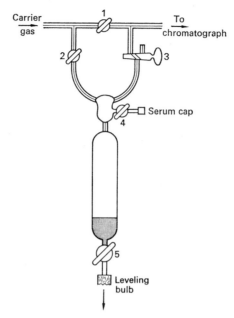

FIG. 79. Vacuum extraction apparatus (Roxburgh, *Canad. J. Microbiol.* **8,** 221 (1962)).

was then transferred to the chromatograph. Because of the low pressure and the small area of contact in the capillary, the rate of readsorption was very slow.

A further method employing reduced pressure techniques has been described by Ikels [280]. He used a modified Van Slyke apparatus and a gas chromatograph as a single instrument to determine small volumes of nitrogen dissolved in blood. Inert and chemically reactive gases were extracted followed by absorption of the oxygen and carbon dioxide and finally measurement of the inert gases, chiefly nitrogen, by gas chromatography.

Stripping Techniques

A method which strips continuously and analyses periodically was introduced by Williams and Miller [281] for the analysis of oxygen, and also argon, nitrogen and carbon dioxide in water samples. These authors had observed that an inert gas could strip 95–98% of oxygen in 15–30 sec from 100 ml of a water sample, when the inert gas was flowing at a rate of 500–1000 ml/min.

In their apparatus a cylindrical drum 4 in. long and 2 in. in diameter was mounted with its axis horizontal, and was fitted with water and stripper gas inlet and outlet as shown in Fig. 80. The water was fed in at such a rate that it occupied one-quarter of the total stripper volume. Mylar discs rotated in the stripper and thin films of water spread over their surface were exposed to the stripping gas. Ideally the stripping gas was also the carrier gas (helium), and the rate of gaseous exchange was very high. Helium/water throughput ratios could be as high as 10:1,

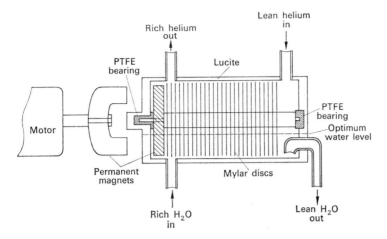

FIG. 80. Apparatus for stripping gaseous components from solution (Williams and Miller, *Analyt. Chem.* **34**, 657 (1962)).

but for the best combination of control and calculation, a ratio of 1:1 was selected. The stripped gas in the helium carrier was fed to a gas sampling valve and injected periodically into the column.

A recent determination of dissolved hydrogen, oxygen, methane, carbon monoxide and carbon dioxide by continuous stripping followed by gas chromatography has been reported by Walker and France [282]. These authors used a method rather similar to that employed by Williams and Miller but which had the advantage of having no moving parts. Essentially the water and helium were passed up a spiral glass tube and the bubble of helium separated at the top of the spiral.

Another method of stripping was used by Swinnerton *et al.* [283]. Their chromatographic assembly included a glass chamber divided into two compartments by a coarse-grade fritted glass disc. The samples were injected through the cap fitted to the top of the chamber. This arrangement is shown in Fig. 81, together with the gas flow system. The liquid sample of about 1–2 ml in volume, was injected into the chamber, the dissolved gases were quickly stripped by the helium carrier gas, dried in the tube containing anhydrous calcium sulphate ("Drierite"), and passed to the chromatographic column. The peaks obtained by this method were slightly wider than those obtained by direct injection of gas on to a column, but no difficulty was experienced in measuring them by planimetry.

This method was extended by Park *et al.* [284] to the determination of carbon dioxide in sea water; bicarbonate and carbonate ions were converted to carbon dioxide by the addition of 2 ml of 0·1 N hydrochloric acid to 3 ml of the sea water followed by stripping.

Tolk *et al.* [285] modified the concentration method of Lewis and Melnick [266], the helium stream carrying the stripped gases being passed through a gas trap fitted with molecular sieve 5A which at liquid nitrogen temperature, adsorbs hydrogen, nitrogen and oxygen from the helium stream. The stripping technique was again a modification of that of Swinerton *et al.* [283].

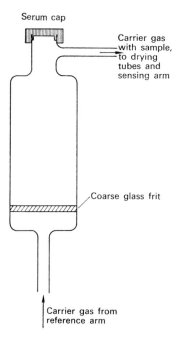

Serum cap

Carrier gas
with sample,
to drying
tubes and
sensing arm

Coarse glass frit

Carrier gas from
reference arm

FIG. 81. Stripping chamber for the recovery of gaseous constituents (after Swinnerton, Linnenbom and Cheek, *Analyt. Chem.* **34**, 483 (1962)).

Direct Injection of the Liquid Sample

The liquid sample material containing the gaseous constituents can be injected directly on to the chromatographic column. The more volatile gases will be separated and eluted from the column in the usual way, whilst the higher boiling compounds that would either not be eluted, or would be eluted with appreciable retention times, can be removed by back flushing. With this method, some pressure controller may be necessary to limit the pressure surge when a large liquid sample is vaporized. This may also be necessary in methods where the liquid phase is converted to a gaseous compound that cannot interfere with the subsequent analyses, as, for example, in the method of Kung *et al.* [286]. In this method the aqueous substrate is converted to acetylene by reaction with calcium carbide in a short pre-column unit.

A short pre-column unit packed with a suitable absorbent can also be used to retain the liquid part of the sample, permitting the gaseous constituents to pass to the chromatographic column. The absorbent material should be chemically inert to both the solvent and the gases evolved, and should not assist or retard the subsequent chromatographic separation.

This technique was successfully used by Kilner and Ratcliff [287] who used a calcium sulphate pre-column in the determination of gases dissolved in water.

CHAPTER 18

Gas Sampling

THE great care necessary to obtain accurate, reproducible results has been stressed throughout this book. This great care is all too frequently wasted by the failure of the person making the collection to ensure that the gas samples are representative of the main bulk of the gas from which they are taken. The British Standards Institution [288, 289] and the Institute of Petroleum [290] have issued details of methods of sampling that should be followed for various types of gaseous mixture, and these recommendations should always be followed wherever practical. There are times when it may be thought to be unnecessary to follow these instructions completely, as, for example, when a chemist is required to take a "one off" sample at short notice. There is no valid excuse, however, for not using a method recommended by one of the official publications of these two bodies. As chemists continue to by-pass these methods it was thought desirable to stress some of the problems of gas sampling and to suggest ways in which some of the unofficial methods in common use can be improved, and thereby provide a more representative sample.

The methods used for taking samples can be summarized and defined as follows:

Snap sample (spot sample): this is a sample taken over an interval of time that is small in comparison with the period during which the gas is flowing.

Continuous sample: this is a sample collected gradually and continuously throughout the period in which the gas is flowing.

Composite snap sample: this is a mixture of snap samples taken at regular intervals from the same sampling point and, like the continuous sample, can be said to be representative of the average conditions for the whole of the specified period of time.

In addition, it is useful also to define gas samples as either wet or dry. These definitions being taken from the recommendations of the Institute of Petroleum [290].

Wet gas is a gas of such composition that small changes of temperature and pressure can cause appreciable changes in composition of the gas by formation of a liquid phase. An example is a gas mixture composed largely of C_3 and C_4 hydrocarbons.

Dry gas is a gas of such composition that large changes of temperature and pressure will not result in the formation of a liquid phase. Examples include mixtures of the permanent gases, including C_1 and C_2 hydrocarbons.

Many other mixtures could be given as examples of dry gases; wet gases are not so numerous, but include also mixtures containing certain freons, chlorinated hydrocarbons and phosgene.

The ideal sample is one that has the mean composition of the total quantity of gas passing along the main pipe from which the sample is taken. The problems that arise in taking a sample from this pipe will depend upon the conditions existing in it. Thus the gas stream may not be constant in composition across any section of this main pipe—a phenomenon referred to as stratification. The wider the pipe and the lower the gas velocity, the greater is the possibility that stratification will occur. In addition, the gas velocity along the pipe may vary, in which case the rate of withdrawal of continuous small quantities of gas should follow proportionally the changes of gas velocity along the pipe. If samples are taken simultaneously at different points along a main gas stream, then allowance must be made for any change in the gas velocity along the pipe, occasioned by the removal of gas samples.

Problems arise not only from the conditions prevailing in the gas stream, but also as a result of changes in the composition of the sample as it is being taken. The most common cause of composition changes during sampling is contamination with air. Other common errors are those arising from a chemical or physical reaction between the material of the sampling system and one or more of the sample components, and the condensation of water in the system, leading to the possibility of losses in solution.

The attack of metal components by corrosive gases is a fairly obvious change of composition, not so well known but even more common is the solution of certain gases in stopcock grease. This effect is so extensive with hydrocarbons and halogenated hydrocarbons that substitutes have been recommended for the usual stopcock greases. These can easily be made in the laboratory—that for use with halogenated hydrocarbons has been given earlier, whilst that for hydrocarbons contains anhydrous glycerol, starch and mannitol in the proportions 100:29:14 by weight. Both of these special greases will absorb water and carbon dioxide, and it is therefore better to use stopcocks with PTFE barrels or seals. Natural rubber absorbs hydrocarbon gases, and this material should never be used to transfer gaseous mixtures containing hydrocarbon gases from a sample line. The condensation of water in gas sample tubes is often completely ignored. This leads to errors in composition arising from the solution of some at least of the carbon dioxide, and probably most of the sulphur dioxide present.

Two further important and often unappreciated or ignored causes of composition changes concern two individual gases, hydrogen and sulphur dioxide. Hydrogen will diffuse rapidly through rubber and certain forms of plastic tubing in common laboratory use, with consequent loss of hydrogen. Moreover, air will often diffuse through the tubing to replace the hydrogen. Sulphur dioxide will not only dissolve in any water that condenses, but will adsorb on to the walls of any glass vessel, and so give low results on analysis. It is virtually impossible to determine this gas, except by using continuous flow methods, or by adsorbing the sample on a solid material and then desorbing *in toto*.

Wherever possible gas samples should *not* be collected by the displacement of water. Where aqueous displacement is to be used, the water should be replaced by brine, sodium sulphate solution or dilute acid—the solution selected being first saturated with the gas to be sampled, before any attempt is made to collect the final sample. Mercury can also be used as a displacement fluid, but should be avoided if the gas stream contains hydrogen sulphide or nitrogen dioxide, both of which can be absorbed.

The errors that can arise from the causes outlined in the preceding paragraphs are common to both wet and dry gases. When taking a sample of a wet gas it is advisable to make sure that about 10% of the total volume of the sample container is left filled with the containing liquid when the gas supply is cut off. This remaining liquid is then drained from the tube after it has been removed from the gas source, thus leaving the gas sample below the pressure of the source in a condition where condensation due to changes in ambient conditions is unlikely.

Sampling probes are normally made of metal, refractory material or of heat-resistant glass. Mild steel probes should not be used above 300°, if oxidation is to be avoided. But where there is no likelihood of chemical reaction, alloy steels can be used to a temperature of 1100°. The manufacturer's advice concerning any particular material may be of value, in that certain compositions will withstand a hot reducing atmosphere, but not an oxidizing one, and vice versa.

The usual materials for refractory probes are fused silica 900°, porcelain 1400°, aluminous porcelain 1100°, mullite 1700°, and recrystallized alumina 1900°—the temperatures indicated being the maximum at which they should be used for this purpose.

Sample probes should be maintained at a sufficiently high temperature to ensure that no component can condense in it. This is particularly important for gases containing water vapour, as not only may the water condense and dissolve certain constituents, to give low results, but may also give rise to erratic results if any of the condensate is blown into subsequent samples.

Method of Taking a Snap Sample

The gas tube should be filled with a suitable fluid—in most cases mercury is the best fluid to use—and connected to the sampling probe with a butt joint. The gas should now be purged along the probe and vented to the atmosphere via the by-pass of the stopcock on the top of the gas tube. The gas flow can now be diverted to the gas tube by rotating the top stopcock and at the same time opening the bottom stopcock to allow the mercury to run out. When all the mercury has transferred from the tube, close the bottom stopcock, and turn the top stopcock to vent the gas to the by-pass once again. The gas supply can now be disconnected.

Method of Taking a Continuous Sample

The easiest way of taking a continuous sample at a substantially constant rate is to mark the sides of a gas tube with calibration marks, and simply to allow mercury to drop from the bottom stopcock at a constant rate. As the head of mercury falls it will be necessary to adjust the rate of escape of the mercury. An alternative procedure is to connect a suitable clockwork or electric motor to a mercury reservoir, and lower this at a constant rate determined by the gearing between the two.

It is an obvious advantage when dealing with dry gases to transport the sample at a pressure slightly above atmospheric, but without mercury present in the tube. This is easily arranged by using two gas tubes in series. Extra gas can now be pushed into the first tube by raising the reservoir to the second.

Method of Taking Composite Snap Samples

This involves running out small amounts of mercury from the gas sample tube at regular intervals during the required sampling period.

Method Using Adsorbents

Lidzey and Longmaid [291] used a concentration method for sampling traces of toxic gases in air involving adsorption on a solid material. The air to be sampled was drawn at a known rate and for a known time through an adsorber (e.g. silica gel treated with suitable reagent). This method can be extended to concentrate many gases by passing them through an adsorbent held at a reduced temperature. The gas can then be subsequently released by elevating the temperature. Care is essential to ensure that the pressure in the adsorbing vessel does not build up as the temperature is increased.

References

1. Martin, A. J. P. and Synge, R. L. M., *Biochem. J.* **35,** 1358 (1941).
2. James, A. T. and Martin, A. J. P., *Biochem. J.* **50,** 679 (1952).
3. *Standards for Petroleum and its Products*, Part I, p. 732. Institute of Petroleum, London, 1967 (26th ed.).
4. Timms, D. G., Konrath, H. J. and Chirnside, R. C., *Analyst,* **83,** 603 (1958).
5. Haraldson, L. and Thorneman, T., *Mikrochim. Ichnoanal. Acta,* 14 (1963).
6. Pratt, G. L. and Purnell, J. H., *Analyt. Chem.* **32,** 1213 (1960).
7. Kipping, P. J. and Jeffery, P. G., *Analyst,* **86,** 680 (1961).
8. British Standard Specification No. 2069 (1954).
9. Peterson, D. L. and Lundberg, G. W., *Analyt. Chem.* **33,** 652 (1961).
10. Karasek, F. W. and Ayers, B. O., *J. Inst. Soc. Amer.* **7,** 70 (1960).
11. Pine, C. S. F., *Talanta,* **14,** 277 (1967).
12. McEwen, D. J., *J. Chromatog.* **9,** 266 (1962).
13. Glew, D. N. and Young, D. M., *Analyt. Chem.* **30,** 1890 (1958).
14. Russell, D. S. and Bednas, M. E., *Analyt. Chem.* **29,** 1562 (1957).
15. Jeffery, P. G. and Kipping, P. J., *Analyst,* **87,** 379 (1962).
16. Jeffery, P. G. and Kipping, P. J., unpublished work.
17. Wilkinson, J. and Hall, D., *J. Chromatog.* **10,** 239 (1963).
18. Berry, R., *Proc. 4th Symp. Gas Chromatog.* Hamburg 1962, p. 321. Butterworths, London (1963).
19. Kipping, P. J. and Winter, D. G., *Nature,* **205,** 1002 (1965).
20. Keulemans, A. I. M., *Gas Chromatography*, Ed. Verver, C. G., p. 58. Reinhold, New York (1957).
21. Rossi, C., Munari, S., Cengarle, L. and Tealdo, G. F., *Chim. e ind.* **42,** 724 (1960).
22. Friedrich, K., *J. Chromatog.* **2,** 664 (1959).
23. Scott, C. G., *J. Inst. Petroleum,* **45,** 118 (1959).
24. Hewett, D. R., unpublished work.
25. Graven, W. M., *Analyt. Chem.* **31,** 1197 (1959).
26. Hollis, O. L., *Analyt. Chem.* **38,** 309 (1966).
27. Wilhite, W. F. and Hollis, O. L., *J. Gas Chromatog.* **6,** 84 (1968).
28. Beuerman, D. R. and Meloan, C. E., *Analyt. Chem.* **34,** 319 (1962).
29. Adams, D. F. and Koppe, R. K., *Tappi,* **41,** 366 (1958).
30. Grune, W. N., *Water Sewage Works,* **107,** 396 (1960).
31. Grune, W. N. and Chueh, C. F., *Int. J. Air Water Poll.* **6,** 283 (1962).
32. Adlard, E. R. and Hill, D. W., *Nature,* **186,** 1045 (1960).
33. Van Der Weil, A., *Nature,* **187,** 142 (1960).
34. Eggertsen, F. T. and Nelson, F. M., *Analyt. Chem.* **30,** 1040 (1958).
35. Hamilton, L. M. and Kory, R. C., *J. Appl. Physiol.* **15,** 829 (1960).
36. Bradford, B. W., Harvey, D. and Chalkley, D. E., *J. Inst. Petroleum,* **41,** 80 (1955).
37. Bua, E., Manaresi, P. and Motta, L., *Analyt. Chem.* **31,** 1910 (1959).
38. Martin, A. J. P., *Vapour Phase Chromatography*, London 1956, p. 2. Butterworths, London (1957).
39. Golay, M. J. E., *Gas Chromatography*, Ed. Coates, V. J. *et al.* p. 1. Academic Press, New York (1958).

40. LOVELOCK, J. E., *Nature*, **182**, 1663 (1958).
41. McWILLIAM, I. G. and DEWAR, R. A., *Proc. 2nd Symp. Gas Chromatog.* Amsterdam 1958, p. 142. Butterworths, London (1958).
42. SCOTT, R. P. W. and CUMMING, C. A., *Proc. 3rd Symp. Gas Chromatog.* Edinburgh 1960, p. 117. Butterworths, London (1960).
43. MOHNKE, M. and SAFFERT, W., *Proc. 4th Symp. Gas Chromatog.* Hamburg 1962, p. 216. Butterworths, London (1963).
44. SCHWARTZ, R. D., BRASSEAUX, D. J. and SHOEMAKE, G. R., *Analyt. Chem.* **35**, 496 (1963).
45. PURCELL, J. E., *Nature*, **201**, 1321 (1964).
46. PETITJEAN, D. L. and LEFTHAULT, C. L., JR., *J. Gas Chromatog.* **3**, 18 (1963).
47. SCHNEIDER, W. and BRUDERRECK, H., *Analyt. Chem.* **36**, 1533 (1964).
48. MARTIN, A. J. P. and JAMES, A. T., *Biochem. J.* **63**, 138 (1956).
49. BOER, H., *Vapour Phase Chromatography, 1956*, p. 169. Butterworths, London (1957).
50. GRANT, D. W., *Proc. 2nd Symp. Gas Chromatog.* Amsterdam 1958, p. 153. Butterworths, London (1958).
51. GRANT, D. W. and VAUGHAN, G. A., *Vapour Phase Chromatography 1956*, p. 413. Butterworths, London (1957).
52. THORBURN, S., Inform. Symp. Gas Chromatog. Discussion Group, Salford, England (1962).
53. BEVAN, S. C., GOUGH, T. A. and THORBURN, S., *J. Chromatog.* **42**, 336 (1969).
54. JANAK, J., *Vapour Phase Chromatography 1956*, p. 247. Butterworths, London (1957).
55. JANAK, J., *Mikrochim. Acta*, 1038 (1956).
56. BOER, H., *Proc. 4th World Petroleum Cong.*, Sect. V/A paper 1, Rome (1955).
57. VAN de CRAATS, F., *Anal. Chim. Acta*, **14**, 136 (1956).
58. HASLAM, J., JEFFS, A. R. and WILLIS, H. A., *Analyst*, **86**, 44 (1961).
59. LANGE, N. A., *Handbook of Chemistry*, p. 1544. Handbook Publ. Inc., Sadusky, Ohio (1956) (9th ed.).
60. RAY, N. H., *J. Appl. Chem.* **4**, 82 (1954).
61. RAY, N. H., *Nature*, **182**, 1663 (1958).
62. LITTLEWOOD, A. B., PHILLIPS, C. S. G. and PRICE, D. T., *J. Chem. Soc.* 1480 (1955).
63. GUILLOT, J., BOTTAZZI, H., GUYOT, A. and TRAMBOUZE, Y., *J. Gas Chromatog.* **6**, 605 (1968).
64. GUILLEMIN, C. L. and AURICOURT, F., *J. Gas Chromatog.* **2**, 156 (1964).
65. HODGMAN, C. D., *Handbook of Chemistry and Physics*, p. 2115. Chemical Rubber Publ. Co., Cleveland, Ohio (1959) (41st ed.).
66. SCOTT, R. P. W., *Nature*, **176**, 793 (1955).
67. SCOTT, R. P. W., *Vapour Phase Chromatography*, London 1956, p. 131. Butterworths, London (1957).
68. WIRTH, M. M., *Vapour Phase Chromatography*, London 1956, p. 154. Butterworths, London (1957).
69. BADDIEL, C. B. and CULLIS, C. F., *Chem. Ind.* 1154 (1960).
70. CRIDER, W. L., *Analyt. Chem.* **37**, 1770 (1965).
71. BRODY, S. S. and CHANEY, J. E., *J. Gas Chromatog.* **4**, 42 (1966).
72. CRIDER, W. L. and SLATER, R. W., JR., *Analyt. Chem.* **41**, 531 (1969).
73. STEVENS, R. K. and O'KEEFE, A. E., *Analyt. Chem.* **42**, 143A (1970).
74. HERSCH, P., *Instr. Practice*, **11**, 817 and 937 (1957).
75. PHILLIPS, T. R., JOHNSON, E. G. and WOODWARD, H., *Analyt. Chem.* **36**, 450 (1964).
76. LIBERTI, A. and CARTONI, C. P., *Gas Chromatography 1958*, p. 321. Butterworths, London (1958).
77. COULSON, D. M. and CAVANAGH, L. A., *Analyt. Chem.* **32**, 1245 (1960).
78. ADAMS, D. F., JENSEN, C. A., STEADMAN, J. P., KOPPE, R. K. and ROBERTSON, T. J., *Analyt. Chem.* **38**, 1094 (1966).
79. COULSON, D. M., *Amer. Lab.* p. 22 (1969).
80. MARTIN, R. L., *Appl. Spectrosc.* **20**, 22 (1966).
81. COULSON, D. M., *J. Gas Chromatog.* **3**, 134 (1965) and **4**, 285 (1966).

82. BURTON, G., LITTLEWOOD, A. B. and WISEMAN, W. A., *Gas Chromatography 1966*, p. 193. Butterworths, London (1966).
83. LITTLEWOOD, A. B. and WISEMAN, W. A., *J. Gas Chromatog.* **5**, 334 (1967).
84. POMPEO, D. J. and OTVOS, J. W., U.S. Pat. 2,641,710 (1953).
85. LOVELOCK, J. E., *Analyt. Chem.* **33**, 162 (1961).
86. OTVOS, J. W. and STEPHENSON, D. P., *J. Amer. Chem. Soc.* **78**, 546 (1956).
87. LOVELOCK, J. E., SHOEMAKE, G. R. and ZLATKIS, A., *Analyt. Chem.* **35**, 460 (1963).
88. LOVELOCK, J. E., *J. Chromatog.* **1**, 35 (1958).
89. LOVELOCK, J. E., JAMES, A. T. and PIPER, E. A., *Ann. New York Acad. Sci.* **72**, 720 (1959).
90. HODGMAN, C. D., *Handbook of Chemistry and Physics*, p. 2551. Chemical Rubber Publ. Co., Cleveland, Ohio (1959) (41st ed.).
91. LOVELOCK, J. E., *Proc. 3rd Symp. Gas Chromatog.* Edinburgh 1960, p. 16. Butterworths, London (1960).
92. GALWEY, A. K., *Talanta*, **9**, 1043 (1962).
93. SHAHIN, M. M. and LIPSKY, S. R., *Analyt. Chem.* **35**, 467 (1963).
94. ROUAYHEB, G. M., FOLMER, O. F. and HAMILTON, W. G., *Anal. Chim. Acta* **26**, 378 (1962).
95. WISEMAN, W. A., *Nature*, **191**, 1187 (1961).
96. BERRY, R. *Nature*,, **188**, 578 (1960).
97. WILLIS, V., *Nature*, **183**, 1754 (1959).
98. ELLIS, J. F. and FORREST, C. W., *Anal. Chim. Acta*, **24**, 329 (1961).
99. LOVELOCK, J. E., *Nature*, **187**, 49 (1960).
100. LOVELOCK, J. E. and LIPSKY, S. R., *J. Amer. Chem. Soc.* **82**, 431 (1960).
101. WASHBROOKE, P. F., Shandon Scientific Co. Ltd. Publ. (1963).
102. LOVELOCK, J. E., *Analyt. Chem.* **35**, 474 (1963).
103. LOVELOCK, J. E., *Nature*, **188**, 401 (1960).
104. HARLEY, J., NEL, W. and PRETORIUS, V., *Nature*, **181**, 177 (1958).
105. DESTY, D. H., GEACH C. J. and GOLDUP, A. *Proc. 3rd Symp. Gas Chromatog.* Edinburgh 1960, p. 46. Butterworths, London (1960).
106. PHILLIPS, T. R. and OWENS, D. R., *Proc. 3rd Symp. Gas Chromatog.* Edinburgh 1960, p. 308. Butterworths, London (1960).
107. McWILLIAM, I. G., *J. Appl. Chem.* **9**, 379 (1959).
108. MIDDLEHURST, J. and KENNETT, B., *Nature*, **190**, 142 (1961).
109. KARMEN, A. and GUIFFRIDA, L. *Nature*, **201**, 1204 (1964).
110. KARMEN, A., *Analyt. Chem.* **36**, 1416 (1964).
111. KARMEN, A., *J. Gas Chromatog.* **3**, 336 (1965).
112. DRESSLER, M. and JANAK, J., *J. Chromatog. Sci.* **7**, 451 (1969).
113. KOKES, R. J., TOBIN, H., JR. and EMMETT, P. H., *J. Amer. Chem. Soc.* **77**, 5860 (1955).
114. GUDZINOWICZ, B. J. and SMITH, W. R., *Analyt. Chem.* **35**, 465 (1963).
115. JEFFERY, P. G. and KIPPING, P. J., *Analyst*, **88**, 266 (1963).
116. BARR, G., *J. Sci. Instr.* **11**, 324 (1934).
117. FRISONE, G. J., *Chem. Analyst*, **54**, 56 (1965).
118. KIPPING, P. J., EDWARDS, V. A. and JEFFERY, P. G., unpublished work.
119. LARD, E. W. and HORN, R. C., *Analyt. Chem.* **32**, 878 (1960).
120. KREJCI, M., TESARIK, K. and JANAK, J., *Gas Chromatography, Instr. Soc. Amer. Symp.* 1959, p. 255. Academic Press, New York (1961).
121. HUNT, P. P. and SMITH, H. A., *J. Phys. Chem.* **64**, 383 (1960).
122. KIPPING, P. J., *Nature*, **191**, 270 (1961).
123. HAMILTON, L. H., *Analyt. Chem.* **34**, 445 (1962).
124. LODGE, J. P., PATE, G. B. and HUITT, H. A., *Chem. Analyst*, **52**, 53 (1963).
125. CUMMINGS, W. G. and REDFEARN, W., *Chem. Ind.* (25) 809 (1957).
126. POLYSCIENCE INC., *J. Gas Chromatog.* **6**, Aug. 8A (1968).
127. HILL, D. W. and NEWELL, H. A., *J. Instr. Sci.* **42**, 783 (1965).
128. BOREHAM, G. R. and MARHOFF, F. A., Gas Council Res. Comm. GC 54 (1958).
129. BAUM, E. H., *Analyt. Chem.* **36**, 438 (1964).
130. MADISON, J. J., *Analyt. Chem.* **30**, 1859 (1958).

131. MOORE, W. R. and WARD, H. R., *J. Amer. Chem. Soc.* **80**, 2909 (1958).
132. RHODES, H. L., *J. Gas Chromatog.* **6**, 488 (1968).
133. *Gas Analysis by Gas Chromatography*, Warren Spring Laboratory, D.S.I.R., Stevenage, England (1962).
134. GLUECKAUF, E. and KITT, G. P., *Vapour Phase Chromatography*, London 1956, p. 422. Butterworths, London (1957).
135. OHKOSHI, S., FUJITA, Y. and KWAN, T., *Bull. Chem. Soc. Japan*, **31**, 770 (1958).
136. REIDEL, O. and UHLMANN, E., *Z. Anal. Chem.* **166**, 433 (1959).
137. GANT, P. L. and YANG, K., *Science*, **129**, 1548 (1959).
138. VENUGOPALAN, M. and KUTSCHKE, K. O., *Canad. J. Chem.* **41**, 548 (1963).
139. PHILLIPS, T. R. and OWENS, D. R., U.K.A.E.A. P.G. Report 419 (CA) (1963).
140. FURUYAMA, S. and KWAN, T., *J. Phys. Chem.* **65**, 190 (1961).
141. CERCY, C., TISTCHNENKO, S. and BOTTER, F., *Bull. Soc. Chim. Fr.* 2315 (1962).
142. SMITH, H. A. and CARTER, E. H., *Tritium in the Physical and Biological Sciences*, p. 121. I.A.E.A., Vienna (1962).
143. CARTER, E. H. and SMITH, H. A., *J. Phys. Chem.* **67**, 535 (1963).
144. KARMEN, A., GIUFFRIDA, L. E. and BOWMAN, R. L., *J. Lipid Res.* **3**, 44 (1962).
145. KARMEN, A., MCCAFFREY, I., WINKELMAN, J. W. and BOWMAN, R. L., *Analyt. Chem.* **35**, 536 (1963).
146. CARTER, E. H., *Dissert. Abstr.* 62–3921, **23**, 1202 (1962).
147. WEST, D. L. and MARSTON, A. L., *J. Amer. Chem. Soc.* **86**, 4731 (1964).
148. GENTY, C. and SCHOTT, R., *Analyt. Chem.* **42**, 7 (1970).
149. CENTI, M. L. and LESIMPLE, M., *J. Chromatog.* **29**, 32 (1967).
150. JANAK, J., *Coll. Czech. Chem. Comm.* **19**, 917 (1954).
151. GREENE, S. A., *Analyt. Chem.* **31**, 480 (1959).
152. WILSON, G. M., FENNEMA, P. J. and STERNER, C. J., *Adv. Cryog. Eng.* **9**, 423 (1964).
153. HAVLENA, E. J., JR. and HUTCHINSON, K. A., *J. Gas Chromatog.* **6**, 419 (1968).
154. PURER, A., *J. Gas Chromatog.* **3**, 165 (1965).
155. LIEBENBERG, D. H., *Analyt. Chem.* **38**, 149 (1966).
156. GIL-AV, E. and HERZBERG-MINZLY, Y., *J. Amer. Chem. Soc.* **81**, 4749 (1959).
157. BOMBAUGH, K. J., *Nature*, **197**, 1102 (1963).
158. FARRÉ-RIUS, F. and GUIOCHON, G., *J. Gas Chromatog.* **1**, 33 (1963).
159. PATTON, H. W., LEWIS, J. S. and KAYE, W. I., *Analyt. Chem.* **27**, 170 (1955).
160. HORTON, A. D., *Nuclear Sci. Eng.* **13**, 103 (1962).
161. OBERMILLER, E. L. and CHARLIER, G. O., *J. Gas Chromatog.* **6**, 446 (1968).
162. SOLOMON, P., *J. Chromatog.* **30**, 593 (1967).
163. MANKA, D. P., *Analyt. Chem.* **36**, 480 (1964).
164. TERRY, J. O. and FUTRELL, J. H., *Analyt. Chem.* **37**, 1165 (1965).
165. BOCOLA, W., BRUNER, F. and CARTONI, G. P., *Nature*, **209**, 200 (1965).
166. BRUNER, F. and DICORCIA, A., *J. Chromatog.* **45**, 304 (1969).
167. ANON., *J. Proc. Inst. Sewage Purification*, Part 3, p. 261 (1962).
168. MORTIMER, J. V., *Proc. 3rd Symp. Gas Chromatog.*, Edinburgh 1960, p. 353. Butterworths, London (1960).
169. PORTER, K. and VOLMAN, D. H., *Analyt. Chem.* **34**, 748 (1962).
170. HESSE, G. and TSCHACHOTIN, B., *Naturwiss.* **30**, 387 (1942).
171. CLAESSON, S., *Arkiv. Kemi.*, **23**, 1 (1947).
172. EGGERTSEN, F. T., KNIGHT, H. S. and GROENNINGS, S., *Analyt. Chem.* **28**, 303 (1956).
173. MCTAGGART, N. G., MILLER, C. A. and PEARCE, B., *J. Inst. Petroleum*, **54**, 265 (1968).
174. JACOBS, E. S., *Analyt. Chem.* **28**, 43 (1966).
175. DAVE, S. B., *J. Chromatog. Sci.* **7**, 398 (1969).
176. BRUNER, F. and CARTONI, G. P., *J. Chromatog.* **18**, 390 (1965).
177. FREDERICKS, E. M. and BROOKS, F. R., *Analyt. Chem.* **28**, 297 (1956).
178. LEE, E. K. C. and ROWLAND, F. S., *Analyt. Chem.* **36**, 2181 (1964).
179. MCKENNA, T. A., JR. and IDLEMAN, J. A., *Analyt. Chem.* **31**, 2000 (1959).
180. MCKENNA, T. A., JR. and IDLEMAN, J. A., *Analyt. Chem.* **32**, 1299 (1960).

181. KONTOROVITCH, L. M., IOGANSEN, A. V., LEVCHENKO, G. T., SEMINA, G. N., BOBROVA, V. P. and STEPANOVA, V. A., *Zavod. Lab.* **28,** 146 (1962).

182. VIGDERGAUZ, M. S., GOL'BERT, K. A., SAVINA, I. M., AFANAS'EV, M. I., ZIMIN, R. A. and BAKHAREVA, N. T., *Zavod. Lab.* **28,** 149 (1962).

183. AVERILL, W. and ETTRE, L. S., *Nature,* **196,** 1198 (1962).

184. PETITJEAN, D. C. and LEFTAULT, C. J., JR., *J. Gas Chromatog.* **1,** 18 (1963).

185. KENT, T. B., *Chem. Ind.* (41), 1260 (1960).

186. KIPPING, P. J. and JEFFERY, P. G., unpublished work.

187. DIETZ, R. N., *Analyt. Chem.* **40,** 1576 (1968).

188. MARVILLET, L. and TRANCHANT, J., *Proc. 3rd Symp. Gas Chromatog.*, Edinburgh 1960, p. 321. Butterworths, London (1960).

189. SMITH, D. H. and CLARK, E., *Proc. Soil Sci. Soc. Amer.* **24,** 111 (1960).

190. SZULCZEWSKI, D. H. and HIGUCHI, T., *Analyt. Chem.* **29,** 1541 (1957).

191. SALTZMAN, B. E. and GILBERT, N., *Amer. Ind. Hygiene Assoc. J.* **20,** 379 (1959).

192. GREENE, S. A. and PUST, H., *Analyt. Chem.* **30,** 1039 (1958).

193. MORRISON, M. E., RINKER, R. G. and CORCORAN, W. H., *Analyt. Chem.* **36,** 2256 (1964).

194. BETHEA, R. M. and ADAMS, F. S., JR., *J. Chromatog.* **10,** 1 (1963).

195. HILL, D. W., *Proc. 3rd Symp. Gas Chromatog.*, Edinburgh 1960, p. 344. Butterworths, London (1960).

196. TROWELL, J. M., *Analyt. Chem.* **37,** 1152 (1965).

197. SZE, Y. L., BORKE, M. L. and OTTERSTEIN, D. M., *Analyt. Chem.* **35,** 240 (1963).

198. AMELL, A. R., LAMPREY, D. S. and SCHIEK, R. C., *Analyt. Chem.* **33,** 1805 (1961).

199. JAMES, A. T., MARTIN, A. J. P. and SMITH, G. H., *Biochem. J.* **52,** 238 (1952).

200. BURKS, R. E., JR., BAKER, E. B., CLARK, P., ERLINGER, J. and LACEY, J. C., JR., *J. Agric. Food Chem.* **7,** 778 (1959).

201. HUGHES, R. B., *J. Sci. Food Agric.* **10,** 431 (1959).

202. JAMES, A. T., *Biochem. J.* **52,** 242 (1952).

203. WOLFRAM, M. L. and ARSENAULT, G. P., *J. Amer. Chem. Soc.* **82,** 2819 (1960).

204. WOOLMINGTON, K. G., *J. Appl. Chem.* **11,** 114 (1961).

205. ISBELL, R. E., *Analyt. Chem.* **35,** 255 (1963).

206. CROPPER, F. R. and KAMINSKY, S., *Analyt. Chem.* **35,** 735 (1963).

207. SCHNEIDER, C. R. and FREUND, H., *Analyt. Chem.* **34,** 69 (1962).

208. HALL, H. L., *Analyt. Chem.* **34,** 61 (1962).

209. NAUGHTON, J. J., HEALD, E. F. and BARNES, T. L., JR., *J. Geophys. Res.* **68,** 539 (1963).

210. WHITSON, R. L. and FOURROUX, M. M., *I.S.A. J.* **7,** 40 (1960).

211. FOX, J. E., *Proc. Soc. Exp. Biol. Med.* **97,** 236 (1958).

212. SCHOLS, J. A., *Analyt. Chem.* **33,** 359 (1961).

213. ADAMS, D. F. and KOPPE, R. K., *Tappi,* **42,** 601 (1959).

214. RYCE, S. A. and BRYCE, W. A., *Analyt. Chem.* **29,** 925 (1957).

215. BOND, R. L., MULLIN, W. J. and PINCHIN, F. J., *Chem. Ind.* 1902 (1963).

216. BERSIN, L. R., BRONSAIDES, F. J. and HOMMEL, C. O., *J. Air Poll. Control Assoc.* **12,** 129 (1962).

217. BRINKMAN, H., *Chem. Tech.* (*Berlin*), **17,** 168 (1965).

218. ROBBINS, L. A., BETHEA, R. M. and WHEELOCK, T. D., *J. Chromatog.* **13,** 361 (1964).

219. ELLIS, J. F., FORREST, C. W. and ALLEN, P. L., *Anal. Chim. Acta,* **22,** 27 (1960).

220. LYSYJ, I. and NEWTON, P. J., *Analyt. Chem.* **35,** 90 (1963).

221. IVESON, G. and HAMLIN, A. G., *Proc. 3rd Symp. Gas Chromatog.*, Edinburgh 1960, p. 333. Butterworths, London (1960).

222. TURKEL'TAUB, N. M., AINSHTEIN, S. A. and SYAVTSILLO, S. V., *Zavod. Lab.* **28,** 141 (1962).

223. ELLIS, J. F. and IVESON, G., *Proc. 2nd Symp. Gas Chromatog.*, Amsterdam 1958, p. 300. Butterworths, London (1958).

224. FISH, A., FRANKLIN, N. H. and POLLARD, R. T., *J. Appl. Chem.* **13,** 506 (1963).

225. ROCHEFORT, O., *Anal. Chim. Acta,* **29,** 350 (1963).

226. DRENNAN, G. A. and MATULA, R. A., *J. Chromatog.* **34,** 77 (1968).

227. HARRISON, G. F., *Vapour Phase Chromatography*, London 1956, p. 332. Butterworths, London (1957).
228. MONKMAN, J. L. and DUBOIS, L., *Gas Chromatog. Instr. Soc. Amer. Symp.* 1959, p. 333. Academic Press, New York (1961).
229. U.S. Fed. Specif. BB-F 671a (3 July 1952), "Freon gas compressed".
230. POLLARD, F. H. and HARDY, C. J., *Vapour Phase Chromatography*, London 1956, p. 115. Butterworths, London (1957).
231. GREEN, S. W., *Vapour Phase Chromatography*, London 1956, p. 300. Butterworths, London (1957).
232. GOL'DINOV, A. L., LUKHOVITSKII, V. I. and SVINNA, N. A., *Zavod. Lab.* **28**, 150 (1962).
233. HALASZ, I. and HORVATH, C., *Nature*, **197**, 71 (1963).
234. GREENE, S. A. and WACHI, F. M., *Analyt. Chem.* **35**, 928 (1963).
235. GREGORY, N. L., *Nature*, **196**, 162 (1962).
236. HASKIN, J. F., WARREN, G. W., PREISTLY, L. J. and YARBOROUGH, V. A., *Advances in Gas Chromatography*, ACS Symp., New York D-135, 1957, Amer. Chem. Soc.
237. TAKAYAMA, Y., *J. Chem. Soc. Japan, Ind. Chem. Sect.* **61**, 682 (1958).
238. SKRIVEN, J. F. and HOELSCHER, H. E., *Amer. Inst. Chem. Eng. J.* **5**, 348 (1959).
239. CAIN, E. F. C. and STEVENS, M. R., *Gas Chromatog. Instr. Soc. Amer. Symp.* 1959, p. 343. Academic Press, New York (1961).
240. BROWNING, L. C. and WATTS, J. O., *Analyt. Chem.* **29**, 24 (1957).
241. YAJIMA, S., SHIBA, K., HANDA, M. and TAKAHASHI, Y., *Bull. Chem. Soc. Japan*, **37**, 800 (1964).
242. STARSHOV, I. M. and VOEVODKIN, Y. P., *Neft. i Neftekim: Nauchn-Tekhn. Sb.* (7), 48 (1965).
243. CARLSTON, A. A., SPENCER, C. F. and JOHNSON, J. F., *Analyt. Chem.* **32**, 1056 (1962).
244. ETTRE, K. and VARADI, P. F., *Analyt. Chem.* **34**, 752 (1962).
245. BORER, K. and PHILLIPS, C. G. S., *Proc. Chem. Soc.* 189 (1959).
246. PHILLIPS, C. G. S., POWELL, P. and SEMLYEN, J. A., *J. Chem. Soc.* 1202 (1963).
247. MYERS, H. W. and PUTNAM, R. F., *Analyt. Chem.* **34**, 664 (1962).
248. KAUFMAN, J. J., TODD, J. E. and KOSKI, W. S., *Analyt. Chem.* **29**, 1032 (1957).
249. SEELY, G. R., OLIVER, J. P. and RITTER, D. M., *Analyt. Chem.* **31**, 1993 (1959).
250. RUSSELL, G. A., *J. Amer. Chem. Soc.* **81**, 4825 (1959).
251. KIPPING, P. J. and JEFFERY, P. G., *Res. Devl. Ind.* (9), 46 (1962).
252. BOREHAM, G. R. and MARHOFF, F. A., *Proc. 3rd Symp. Gas Chromatog.*, Edinburgh 1960, p. 412. Butterworths, London (1960).
253. HILL, R. L. and SONLEY, J. M., *Lab. Pract.* **17**, 55 (1968).
254. FISHER SCIENTIFIC CO. TECH. DATA BULL. TD-151, *Gas Chromatog. Bull.* **8.**
255. FORSEY, R. R., *J. Gas Chromatog.* **6**, 555 (1968).
256. VIZARD, G. S. and WYNNE, A., *Analyst*, **87**, 810 (1962).
257. BAKER, A. R. and HARTWELL, F. J., *Safety in Mines Res. Estab. Rept.* 189 (1960).
258. FELLS, I., HOWELLS, T. J. and PATRICK, M. A., *J. Inst. Fuel*, **34**, 283 (1961).
259. JEFFERY, P. G. and KIPPING, P. J., *J. Inst. Mech. Eng.* **76**, 25 (1966).
260. KASHIMA, J. and YAMAGAKI, T., *Rept. Castings Res. Lab. Woseda Univ.* (*Tokyo*), (10), 89 (1959).
261. KASHIMA, J. and YAMAGAKI, T., *Rept. Castings Res. Lab. Woseda Univ.* (*Tokyo*), (11), 51 (1960).
262. KOCH, W. and LEMM, H. *Arch. Eisenhuettenw.* **38** (12), 881 (1967).
263. KASHIMA, J. and YAMAGAKI, T., *Japan Analyst*, **12**, 347 (1963).
264. BRYAN, F. R. and BONFIGLIO, S., *J. Gas Chromatog.* **2**, 97 (1964).
265. WINGE, R. K. and FASSEL, V. A., *Analyt. Chem.* **37**, 67 (1965).
266. LEWIS, L. C. and MELNICK, L. M., *Analyt. Chem.* **34**, 868 (1962).
267. GALWEY, A. K., *Talanta*, **10**, 310 (1963).
268. JURANEK, J. and AMBROVA, A., *Coll. Czech. Chem. Comm.* **25**, 2814 (1960).
269. HILLEN, L. W. and THACKRAY, M., *J. Chromatog.* **10**, 309 (1963).
270. CARPENTER, F. G., *Analyt. Chem.* **34**, 66 (1962).
271. JEFFERY, P. G. and WILSON, A. D., *Analyst*, **85**, 749 (1960).

272. DUSWALT, A. A. and BRANDT, W. W., *Analyt. Chem.* **32,** 272 (1960).
273. PARSONS, M. L., PENNINGTON, S. N. and WALKER, J. M., *Analyt. Chem.* **35,** 842 (1963).
274. REITSEMA, R. H. and ALLPHIN, N. L., *Analyt. Chem.* **33,** 355 (1961).
275. JEFFERY, P. G. and KIPPING, P. J., *Analyst,* **87,** 594 (1962).
276. CURRY, A. S., HURST, G., KENT, N. R. and POWELL, M., *Nature,* **195,** 603 (1962).
277. ELSEY, P. G., *Analyt. Chem.* **31,** 869 (1959).
278. NATELSON, S. and STELLATE, R. L., *Analyt. Chem.* **35,** 847 (1963).
279. ROXBURGH, J. M., *Canad. J. Microbiol.* **8,** 221 (1962).
280. IKELS, K. G., *J. Gas Chromatog.* **3,** 359 (1965).
281. WILLIAMS, D. D. and MILLER, R. R., *Analyt. Chem.* **34,** 657 (1962).
282. WALKER, J. A. J. and FRANCE, E. D., *Analyst,* **94,** 364 (1969).
283. SWINERTON, J. W., LINNENBOM, V. J. and CHEEK, C. H., *Analyt. Chem.* **34,** 483 (1962).
284. PARK, K., KENNEDY, G. H. and DOBSON, H. H., *Analyt. Chem.* **36,** 1686 (1964).
285. TOLK, A., LINGERAK, W. A., KONT, A. and BORGER, A., *Anal. Chim. Acta,* **45,** 137 (1969).
286. KUNG, J. T., WHITNEY, J. E. and CAVAGNOL, J. C., *Analyt. Chem.* **33,** 1505 (1961).
287. KILNER, A. A. and RATCLIFF, G. A., *Analyt. Chem.* **36,** 1615 (1964).
288. *Methods for the Sampling and Analysis of Fuel Gases*, Brit. Standard 3156 (1959).
289. *Methods for the Sampling and Analysis of Fuel Gases*, Part I, Brit. Standard 1756: Part I (1963).
290. INSTITUTE OF PETROLEUM, *Standards for Petroleum and Its Products*, Part IV, Methods for Sampling (2nd. ed) (1962).
291. LIDZEY, R. G. and LONGMAID, F. M., *Chem. Ind.* 150 (1964).

Author Index

Subject Index